AF552615

Management of Wastelands

Volume - I

Identification and Distribution

Volume. I : Identification and Distribution
Volume. II : Problems and Prospects
Volume. III : Reclamation and Development

About the Editor

Hridai R. Yadav, an Eminent Scientist obtained degrees of M.Phil., Ph.D. from Jawahar Lal Nehru University, New Delhi, worked with CSIR Government of India as Research Scientist and Pool Scientist for eight years having authored 6 books and 63 research papers. He has been the Member of National Wastelands Development Board, Government of India and nominated as UGC observer for the selection of Professor in the various Universities and UGC nominee in the Board of Management of Autonomous Institute of Engineering and Technology (GBTU), Lucknow. H.R. Yadav has been the Member of various Government and Autonomous Institutions/Universities, besides being Founder-Member-Secretary-Director of the Institute of Wastelands Reclamation and Rural Development (1990), Institute of Science and Technology for Rural Development (1994) and UGC accredited RIWARD Post Graduate College, Hanumanganj, Sultanpur, U.P. (2004). Presently, H.R. Yadav is engaged in the implementation of Agro-Afforestation on Patta Banjar Land alloted to Scheduled Caste Community, Women Empowerment and Rural Health Mission Programmes in Amethi.

Management of Wastelands

Volume -I

Identification and Distribution

Edited by
Hridai R. Yadav

CONCEPT PUBLISHING COMPANY PVT. LTD.
NEW DELHI-110059

ISBN-13 : 978-81-8069-943-6 (Set)
978-81-8069-944-3 (Vol. I)
978-81-8069-945-0 (Vol. II)
978-81-8069-946-7 (Vol. III)

First Published 2013

Published and Printed by

Concept Publishing Company Pvt. Ltd.
A/15-16, Commercial Block, Mohan Garden
New Delhi-110059 (India)
T: 25351460, 25351794, *F*: 091-11-25357109
E: publishing@conceptpub.com, W: www.conceptpub.com
Editorial Office: H-13, Bali Nagar, New Delhi-110 015, India.

Cataloging in Publication Data--*Courtesy:* D.K. Agencies (P) Ltd <docinfo@dkagencies.com>

Management of wastelands / edited by Hridai R. Yadav.
3 v. cm.
Includes bibliographical references and indexes.
Contents: v. 1. Identification and distribution — v. 2. Problems and prospects— v.3. Reclamation and development.
ISBN 9788180699436 (set)
ISBN 9788180699443 (v. 1)
ISBN 9788180699450 (v. 2)
ISBN 9788180699467 (v. 3)

1. Waste lands—India—Management. I. Yadav, Hridai Ram, 1957-

DDC 333.730954 23

Dedicated

To

My Publishing Mentor

Late Shri Naurang Rai Ji

Preface

It has been realized that ever increasing demand for Fuel Wood, Fodder, Fiber, Fruits, Fisheries and Food Grains (F^6), of the growing population and increasing needs of the raw materials for the Industries has led to environmental degradation and rapid expansion of wastelands. It has been noted that out of the total land mass of 328 million hectares of our country, 175 million hectares land are degraded. The land degradation is mostly caused by the poverty and mismanagement of land. The degradation of natural land resources proceeds from hacking, overgrazing, excessive agricultural cropping, overirrigation and excess use of fertilizers, mismanagement and natural calamities etc. has caused land degradation. The Satellite imagery has indicated that we are loosing 1.3 million hectares of forest every year. The fire wood requirement is 130 million tonnes per year out of which we are fetching about 50 million tonnes per year from forest and 80 million tonnes balance fire wood requirements has yet to be generated. The larger revenue raised through unplanned and unscientific cutting of forest, the greater destruction of forest area and it has to be stopped.

Article 48-A of the Constitution of India enunciates, "The State shall endeavour to protect and improve the environment and to safeguard the forest and wildlife of the country". For the fulfilment of this objective, the task of environmental protection has become of prime importance to the nation. The schemes of environmental protection, afforestation, prevention and reclamation of wastelands, better use of irrigation through scientific management and development of alternative sources of rural energy have already been included in the 20-point economic programme.

The major themes for discussion are : (i) identification, definition, classification and distribution of wastelands, (ii) reclamation of wastelands for Agro-afforestation, (iii) water conservation and irrigation management, (iv) environment protection, (v) economics of wastelands development, and (vi) people's participation and generation of awareness, policy planning strategies.

Wastelands problem is mostly man-made and causes misery to millions of the rural poor. Thus reclamation of wastelands may be adopted as a strategy for the extension of net sown area according to its suitability to increase the total agricultural production through cropping or for the plantation programme predominantly for the fulewood and fodder for the overall development of the rural poor. It is felt that there is an immense need : (i) for a comprehensive survey, mapping and identification of wastelands and preparation of an action plan for wastelands reclamation and to create the data base, (ii) to save existing forests by enacting strict laws, (iii) to increase and maintain forest area for industrial use through proper management, (iv) to enhance wood wealth and to meet fodder needs through social forestry. It should also include fruit trees. A coordinated action plan should be drawn for social forestry and Agro-forestry. We must also examine the role and impact of social forestry and the status of actual forests. We cannot allow actual forest to be destroyed and expect social forestry to compensate. It would help to maintain the ecological balance and protection of environment for its longer sustained use by the resourceless village poors.

The importance of the wastelands and land degradation has been stressed by many environmental scientists, ecologists and social scientists. In totality our environmental policy, the proper management of natural resources must take absolute primacy. Management, enrichment and optimum utilization of scarce natural resources are vital prerequisites of a purposeful national strategy for economic development and poverty alleviation.

It was the vision and environmental zeal of Indiraji, that led to her pioneering statement on Environment at the Stockholm Conference. With the subsequent establishment of the Department of Environment, we have gradually come to realize that, in addition to control of industrial pollution and protection of wildlife, we must prevent farther degradation of the country's basic natural resources and endowments, and life support systems of land, water and vegetation. The setting up of the National Wastelands Development Board and

Department of Wastelands Development and later on Department of Land Resources has been formed in the Govt. of India yet another important milestone in the saga of our efforts to prevent environmental degradation and create tree cover over millions, of hectares land, in the process, to promote the economic and social well-being of millions of our people.

The preservation and protection of our environment and forests, cannot secured by statutory measures, governmental control and punitive mechanism. The realization that the preservation and enrichment of our environment and the propagation of our forest cover is an ecological imperative must become ingrained in the national psyche. We must start with the children, in their schools and colleges The awareness that we create now in these young minds that the Tree is India's life and part of it would be an awareness that will reach out into generations in the future as well. In the historic words of Indiraji :

> "In his arrogance with his own increasing knowledge and ability, man has ignored his dependence on the earth and has lost his communion with it. He no longer puts his ear to the ground so that the earth can whisper its secrets to him. The national song which inspired our freedom movement describes our land as one endowed with water and fruit, rich with the greenness of growing plants. We must make this true not only of India but of all lands."

If her dream is to come true, we must no longer confine ourselves to regulations and control to preserve and enrich our natural resources, but each one of us must put his ear to the ground and listen to what Mother Earth asks of him or her. And having listened, each one must do his or her bit for giving back to Mother Earth what centuries of despoliation has taken away so ruthlessly from her.

In view of the above we must respond to generate proper movement for conservation of available wastelands natural resources. Decentralized village peoples nurseries and tissue culture raised plants or hybrid plants, and reclamation of wastelands, plantation of Agro-forestry and social-forestry species and leasing of the land to the interested rural poor on Tree Patta basis for Agro-Afforestation and a comprehensive awareness raising programme should be taken up under the MNREGA Scheme through village Panchayat and the State - Districts - Tehsil - Block and Village Panchayat level Administrative machinery must create an infrastructure and atmosphere conducive to MNREGA Job Card holders to generate employment and to ensure people involvement in the Agri.-Horti.-Forestry programmes at grass root level.

Village Panchayat level *Van Mahotsava* must be re-initiated in corporating the reclamation of wastelands for Agri.-Horti.-Afforestation programmes with the view to meet the increasing demand of growing cattle and human for Fuel Wood, Fodder, Fiber, Fruits, Fisheries and Food Grains (F^6) and to generate employment and increase the income of the deprived resource less rural poor peoples.

In view of the above an attempt has been made to incorporate the various case studies carried out by the agricultural scientists, environmentalists, social workers and policy planners at various levels with the view to provide exchange of views, opinions, experiences for further formulation of peoples participatory planning process for Agri.-Horti.-Afforestation programme through reclamation of wasteland natural resources to meet the ever increasing demand of growing cattle and human population and also to maintain the ecological imbalances at the grass root level.

It has been realized that the various programme related to soil conservation, wastelands development, environment protection and management, Agri.-Horti.-Afforestation management does not normally percolate the basic strata of the common people living in the remote rural areas has often led to its failure at the grass root level. Hence, a socio-politico, techno-scientific peoples participatory wastelands reclamation for the Agriculture, Horticulture and Social-forestry and environmental management programmes must be initiated at grass root level through peoples participation and the usufructs accrued out of it should be shared by the resourceless deprived rural poor multitudes at village level. The administrative machinery has to be properly involved and the Mahatma Gandhi National Employment Guarantee Act (MNREGA) Scheme should generate 100 days employment for the MNREGA Job Card holders for Reclamation and Conservation of the allotted Patta Banjar land for Fuel Wood, Fodder,

Fibre, Fruits, Fisheries and Food Grains (F^6) to meet the ever increasing demand of growing cattle and human population and to improve the degraded environment of the area and also to improve the socio-economic conditions of the deprived rural poor multitudes living in the remote rural areas.

Prof. (Dr.) Hridai R. Yadav

Acknowledgements

It is known fact that from time immemorial, man has lived in harmony with nature, in a symbiotic relationship with the nature. The nature gave its bounty to man was in return, recompensed adequately by self-regenerating process or eco-development, built into the cultural, social and economic traditions of human life, as an individual and in groups.

In view of the above an attempt has been made to re-capsulate the techno-scientific practical studies carried out on Wastelands identification, distribution and Problems and Prospects of Wastelands and Reclamation and Development of Wastelands, which had been printed in the earlier work, with the view to provide decadal changes in the distribution, problems, prospects, reclamation and policy, planning strategies of the wastelands development at national and grass root level.

We are highly obliged and grateful to all the contributors for their already contributed techno-scientific studies which has been re-capsulated to bring out new volumes of Wastelands for its wider replicability. We acknowledge our sincere gratitudes for all the contributors for their kind support, without their help this re-capsulated work on Wastelands would not have been possible.

We acknowledge our sincere gratitudes to Late Sri Naurang Rai Ji who supported in an integrated manner for publication of Wastelands studies carried by me before to decades.

We are grateful to Sri Ashok Kumar Mittal, CMD, Concept Publishing Co. Pvt. Ltd., New Delhi, to kindly accept the publication of re-capsulated contributions on Wastelands in the Loving Memory of my publishing Mentor Late Sri Naurang Rai Ji.

Last but not the least, I am grateful to my wife Reeta and lovely son Sahit Hridai, without whose support completion of this work would not have been possible.

Prof. (Dr.) Hridai R. Yadav

Introduction

The soul of India lives in the villages. The village common people depends on agriculture and survive on the available forest resources. It has been recorded that out of 328 million hectares land of our country, 175 million hectares land has been degraded. The Satellite imagery has indicated that we are loosing 1.3 million hectares of our forest cover per year. The fire wood requirement has been 130 million tons per year out of which we are fetching only 50 million tons per year from forest and 80 million tons balance fire wood requirement has yet to be generated.

The growing wastelands has brought us face to face socio-economic crisis and ecological imbalances and environmental deterioration. In view of the above an attempt has been made in this study to re-capsulate the research and development, action oriented wastelands distribution, reclamation and development studies carried out by various scientists, social workers and programme implementing institutions with the view to provide a decadal experience in the field of wastelands development.

An attempt has been made to bring out the wastelands development programmes and experiences in three volumes. The First Vol. of the book has been contributed on Identification and Distribution of wastelands, the Second Vol. is related to Problems and Prospects of wastelands while the Third Vol. has been incorporated for the Reclamation and Development of wastelands.

Vol. I	**Wastelands**	Identification and Distribution
Vol. II	**Wastelands**	Problems and Prospects
Vol. III	**Wastelands**	Reclamation and Development

The historical perspectives of the wastelands and the growth of wastelands has been analyzed by H.R. Yadav while the analysis of wastelands in Arid Zone by using Remote Sensing Techniques has been analyzed by K.A. Shankar Narayanan, Amal Kumar Sen and Balak Ram. The identification of wastelands and the various types of wastelands has been analyzed by H.R. Yadav. The problem and prospects of afforestation on salt-affected soils has been analyzed by H.S. Gill and I.P. Abrol. While Arun Chavan has attempted to explain an approach to the wastelands development while the problem of wastelands has been described by H.R. Yadav. The Typology and Mapping Procedures of wastelands in the Indian Arid zone has been explained by Amal Kumar Sen and R.B. Mandal has attempted to explain the problem of wasteland in the district Munger, Bihar. S.C. Srivastava and Banwari Lal have made an effort to explain the Wasteland in Uttar Pradesh : An Analysis of its Pattern, Growth and Strategy for Future Development. N.L. Gupta and (Mrs.) S. Kothari have explained the Wastelands of Rajasthan : A Peep into Changes, 1960-61 to 1984-85. Amal Kumar Sen has explained the Land Utilization, Mapping to Estimate the Wastelands of Arid Zone in Rajasthan by Photo Interpretation Technique. D.R. Bhumbla and Arvind Khare have made an attempt to explain the Estimate of Wastelands in India. A.S. Kolarkar and R.P. Dhir have attempted to explain the Soils of Wastelands and their Potentials in Arid Western Rajasthan. C.T. Abichandani and A.S. Kolarkar and S.V. Goinda Rajan have made an effort to analyze the Wastelands and their better use through soil survey. Thus, an attempt has been made in this Volume to analyze the identification and distribution of wastelands at various levels.

Prof. (Dr.) Hridai R. Yadav

Contents

List of Tables

List of Figures

1

Historical Perspective of Wastelands

Hridai R. Yadav

The concept of wasteland is not a new one. The problem of wasteland has a long history, and it is assumed it was started by the Apeman. It has been felt that in the initial stage the Apeman survived on nature and lived as a barbarian. But a time came when he realized he had lost his ability to catch the animal. Later on by throwing a stone at the animal and disabling it made it possible for him to catch the animal for his food. In the same way, he started developing his technology. This historical incident must have disturbed nature and caused the formation of wasteland according to time, process and stage.

Later on the Apeman started innovating the sharp stone for hunting purposes. In such a technology only a few of them were skilled in killing the animal. In this way, they disturbed nature resulting in desertification and ecological imbalance of wasteland:

(1) Place of collecting the stone.
(2) Place of sharpening (technological manufacturing) the stone.
(3) Place of hunting site.
(4) Place where they killed the animal and the stone thrown.

It has been assumed that the development of wasteland increased with the development of technology; if an Apeman could survive without technology then increase of the wasteland was least possible.

In this regard it has also been assumed that starting from the Apeman and those invaders from outside India to the present we are developing the technology which has become an asset for increasing the wastelands. There is no such document by which the area under wasteland could be analysed for the past.

These historical rulers demarcated the wasteland as the land which was not serving any purpose, in the 4th Century B.C. during the Kalinga War. Our history shows that we were having Anarya system which declined due to increased activity and might-is-right attitude of the upper classes. So the good quality land was in the hands of the upper castes in the plain areas, while the Sudras (low caste people) were thrown in the hilly areas which were demarcated as wasteland (land not available for any purpose).

Emperor Ashoka has also used the wasteland for proper evaluation of land. Ambassador Megasthenese has also used the wasteland as neglected land. In the Moghul Period, Babar also used the term wasteland in different ways, as the neglected land, for purposes of fixing the land value and revenue collection. Later, Akbar the Great during his rule fixed the value of land in Annas to the farmers for the purpose of revenue collection from Talukdars. For poor quality land he charged very nominal land revenue, but for good quality land, according to its productivity, he levied 14 annas to 16 annas while for the neglected land he did not charge anything.

The British also continued the same practice. They did not charge any kind of land revenue for wasteland or the land which failed to yield a positive return to the farmer.

It has been assumed that the development of wasteland started through the triangular force of man, nature and technology. When men himself was interacting with nature for his survival, the concept of wasteland did not exist. But from the period of the Apeman including the sharpening of the stone and hunting of animals, the problem of wasteland started. It may be said that the development of technology has caused an increase in the wasteland but it has also provided all sorts of development oriented to the human being in terms of disease and death. But one cannot say that we should stop the development of technology because it increases the wasteland.

Wasteland : A Serious Issue

Presently, the problem of wasteland has become a serious issue and it has increased with the development of technology for increasing the agricultural production. We are developing a lot of good quality technology to produce efficient tools/machines for our needs. Technological developments need several inputs for which at least 5-6 types of wasteland development are taking place, all of which are disturbing our natural resources in the name of raw material. The place of extraction, the transportation system by which they are brought, the place where they are manufactured, the place where they are distributed among the concentrated people are hurting our environment partially. Thus in a colonized way these processes disturbed the nature in the form of wasteland which has become a problem for everyone. The development of technology, growth of human and cattle population have been involved as a factor for the growth of wasteland. The development of wasteland, in this way, according to Davisian concept, may be explained according to time, process and stage.

The problem of wasteland is a historical phenomenon, which has been used historically to indicate little used common land on less fertile land which failed to yield a return to the cultivators. A layman may define wasteland in a different way, as the land which is lying uninhabited, uncultivated and left after use or land which is no longer serving any purpose. The adjective waste has now disappeared because in many cases such lands are much valued as open spaces. But historically such lands were left as unutilised due to some reason or the other.

Dudley Stamp defined wasteland as the land which has been used previously but which has been abandoned and for which no further use has been found.

The Wasteland Survey and Reclamation Committee defined wastelands as those lands which are either not available for cultivation or left out of cultivation as fallows and cultivable waste. Hence, it includes the following types of land:

(i) Land not available for cultivation, barren and uncultivable waste.

(ii) Other uncultivated land excluding fallows, culturable waste, permanent pastures and land under miscellaneous trees and crops.

(iii) Fallows.

Thus it includes, in the culturable waste, all land available for cultivation but not taken up for cultivation and abandoned after a few years owning to some reason or the other. Such lands may be fallow for more than five years and may be covered with shrubs, and grass lands which are reserved for pasture and not included in culturable waste. Fallows of one year are classified as current fallow and those of one to five years as old fallow. Thus, the wasteland for the purpose of extension of cultivation are confined to other uncultivated land excluding old fallows other than current fallow. Thus, the wasteland is that land which lies uncultivated for the present but has been used previously.

Conclusion

It may be concluded that the problem of wasteland is historical. The development of wasteland increases with the increase of technology. It has got a positive correlation with the man and technology, high doses of technology, and increase in the population has been working as a dominant factor in the development of wasteland leaving the natural factor behind. The natural calamities including droughts, desertification and floods, are also responsible for an increase in the wasteland. The natural disturbances including the man-made problems, i.e. industrialization and urbanization, are contributors to increase the wastelands in various ways. Thus, overall development of technology and growth of human population, cattle population as also the natural disasters are responsible for the loss of our natural resources and land degradation. In this regard, it cannot be concluded that we should stop the development of technology or we should stop the growth of human and cattle population but it may be said that the proper use of technology in the manufacturing and extracting of the natural resources through proper planning and management will be helpful in checking the growth of wastelands. Thus, proper planning before extracting the natural resources, manufacturing and distributing them for the use of the people may be helpful in checking an increase in land degradation. Hence, we should not say that the technological advancement should be stayed or slowed down but it can be suggested that as we are planning for different types of industries and urban colonies on different types of land, according to our increasing demand, we should have a proper planning for such land uses also which will be helpful for the overall management of land utilization and checking the growth of wastelands including man-made and natural problems responsible for an increase of land degradation.

Lastly, it may be said that the wasteland which is increasing at an alarming rate may not be checked only through afforestation but it also needs proper scientific planning of different categories of land use, and proper training, education, demonstration to the users of land. Different types of development programmes related to the wasteland and initiated by the government agencies may be helpful to certain extent but the growth of the wasteland may not be checked without involving the local people, because they are the people who create conditions for an increase in wastelands for their survival out of ignorance and innocence, and this has created the problem of wastelands up to the present extent. Historically, as it has been explained, the Apeman disturbed nature out of ignorance, he was only bothered about filling his belly. So is the state of the present man. He. is also bothered only about his food, shelter and clothing. He is ignorant and innocent of the use and misuse of our natural land resources. The development of wastelands for his use needs a large-scale people's movement and involvement of everyone in this programme. Without their co-operation such programmes cannot be made successful. It is felt that wasteland may be used for fulfilling our requirements of fuelwood, fodder, fruit and foodgrains, for the increasing human and cattle population. Thus, it can be said that the wasteland utilization will be an economic proposition to our economy and overall development of our nation.

REFERENCES

Shafi, M. "The Problems of Wastelands in India", *The Geographer*, Vol. XV, November 1986, AMJ, Geographical Society, Aligarh.

Stamp, L.D. *The Land of Britain: Its Use and Misuse*, 1948, p. 433.

Yadav, H.R. *The Genesis and Utilisation of Wastelands*, 1986, Concept Publishing Co. (P) Ltd., New Delhi.

2

Analysis of Wastelands in Arid Zone by Remote Sensing Techniques*

K.A. Shankarnarayan, Amal Kumar Sen* and *Balak Ram

Introduction

Assessment of use and misuse of land is the prerequisite to plan the utilization of resources. Land utilization survey and mapping is the obvious requirement to make such estimates. The ultimate purpose of land utilization survey and map is to arrive at systems of land use and management best suitable to the kinds of resources and capabilities of the land composing it.

With the background of these principles, the specific problems of the arid zone were considered to standardise the mapping units for land use survey. The problems of arid zone are many and were well discussed and summarised in the proceedings of the symposium on problems of Indian Arid Zone (1972).

Considering these problems of arid zone and on the basis of experiences drawn while conducting land utilization mapping in the region, the scheme for classification of land use units for land use maps was worked out (Table 2.1: Sen. 1974).

---

* Reprinted from proceedings of "Symposium on Resources Survey for Land Use Planning and Environmental Conservation", ISPI & RS, Dehradun, Oct. 20-22, 1982.

Wastelands in Western Rajasthan

Wastelands in western Rajasthan has been mainly classified into four classes: stony, gravelly, saline and sandy wastes. But considering their complexes, biotic interferences and restrictions of uses they have been further classified in course of survey and remote sensing operations and this has been presented in Table 5.2. In western Rajasthan 64,50,476 ha or 33.25 per cent wastelands comprises of various categories.

Table 2.1 : Tentative scheme of land utilization units proposed for arid zone

1. Settlement
   - A. Rural Settlement
     - (a) Villages with compact settlement (unplanned)
     - (b) Villages with scattered settlement (unplanned)
     - (c) Linear compact villages
     - (d) Temporary Villages
     - (e) Deserted villages
   - B. Urban areas
     - (a) Administrative
     - (b) Residential
     - (c) Mining
     - (d) Agricultural
     - (e) Religious centre
2. Water Resources
   - (a) Rivers
   - (b) Place and depressions — salt lakes
   - (c) Wells
     - (i) Deep (ii) Moderately deep (iii) Shallow
   - (d) Tanks
     - (i) Permanent (ii) Seasonal
3. Wastelands (Also come under Pasture Land)
   - (a) Sand waste (including shifting sand dunes)
   - (b) Rocky waste
   - (c) Saline waste
   - (d) Gravelly waste
4. Pasture Land and Grazing Ground
   - (a) Permanent pasture (Oran)
   - (b) Wastelands and current fallows (Suitable representation is to be made so that both are indicated).
   - (c) Hay, thorn, weeds and shrubs — where the grasses are periodically cut.
5. Forest Land
   - (a) Natural forest
     - (i) Thin (ii) Dense
   - (b) Afforested land
   - (c) Plantation (road side, railway side, etc.)

6. Cultivated Land
   (a) Single cropped area
   (b) Double cropped area
   (c) Current fallow (also fall under pasture land and grazing ground)

Wastelands are surface features of the land and as such they appear clearly in photographs (Moutapa, 1972).

Study of pattern aspects and photo elements enable in the arid zone to distinguish hills, sloping hill sides, gravelly lands, sand dunes and depressional areas in the photographs. These comprise wastelands in Indian desert (Sen, 1972). Uncultivated sandy plains and saline lands can also be identified and mapped by photo interpretation. In Indian arid zone we have distinguished four types of wastelands—rocky waste, gravelly waste, sandy waste and saline waste. The photographic characteristics of these waste lands are as follows:

Sandy Waste

Specific photo-pattern is large area covering in a continuous manner often interrupted by hummocks (sand dunes) of varying sizes. The images are marked by contrasted tones. Sandy hills or dunes are identified by complex or unusual forms. Close examination of stereoscopic pairs are necessary. Dunes are often marked by stippled structure and coarse texture; sizes and shapes are irregular. Sandy waste lands often indicate diffused boundary. Aerial photographs of desert region will not show vegetative cover on dunes. Dunes are sometimes mantled by grasses which cover darker tones than barren sand. A dune on a sandy plain may appear white against a dark background.

Rocky Waste

Image structure is mottled, texture is medium to coarse. Specific photo-pattern in large area covering in a continuous manner interrupted by hills and rock outcrops. Scattered trees and shrubs are identified. Distinct or clear boundary of the unit is often identified. The images present contrasted colour and tones.

Gravelly Waste

Specific photo-pattern is large or small area in a continuous manner.

Tone variation is medium to light. The presence of the gravels are marked by close arrangement of dots—course texture in the photo image.

Saline Waste

It is easier to identify and locate saline wastes on the phtographs due to appearance of greyish white or ash coloured tone of the image as a result of salt formation on the surface of the land. In arid zone, the 'playas' or saline depression often form saline wastelands. These can be easily identified in the photographs.

A survey of wastelands without aerial photographs will be a very costly and tremendous task.

Land Use of the Sand Dunes

In previous surveys, dunes were identified and mapped as sandy wastes, but in actual practice, they are not universally sandy wastes. These are rather often cultivated during rainy season. The active sand dunes are universally wastelands. The stabilised dunes are also often wastelands but the lower and middle flanks of these dunes are cultivated in years of very good rainfall, particularly in rainfall zone of over 200 mm. Long fallows of five years duration in 200 mm—300 mm rainfall zone and 2-3 years duration in rainfall zone of over 300 mm are evident. Upper flank and crests of the dunes serve as grazing ground of the livestock. Hence, in sand dunes, three land use units *viz.*, cultivated or cultivable (including short and long fallows), sandy waste and grazing ground can be mapped. But, these details can be mapped only on 1:50,000 scale or above. Such minute details cannot also be readily identified by traditional ground survey. This, however, is possible by aerial photo interpretation—particularly 'edge gradient' study. In order to standardise the photo interpretation techniques to analyse the land use pattern of the sand dunes, studies were conducted with aerial photographs in different areas of Jodhpur, south Bikaner and border areas of Nagaur—Bikaner districts. Study areas were selected, on stratified sample basis, taking the physiographic regions as the units of sampling. Areas so selected, cover 5 to 10 sq km covering 3 to 5 photographs. This has

Table 2.2 : Distribution of Wastelands in Arid Districts of Western Rajasthan (India) (Based on Remote Sensing and Field Surveys) (Area in ha)

Dlistrict	*Sandy waste*	*Saline waste*	*Stony waste*	*Gravelly waste*	*Rocky waste*	*Rocky & stony waste*	*Stony & Gravelly waste*	*Rocky & Gra-velly waste*	*Sandy waste with open scrubs*	*Rocky & Gravelly with open scrubs*	*Total & % to Total Area of the Distt.*
Jaisalmer	900315	95097	–	–	–	58909	–	64111	991960	924031	3034423
%	(24.77)	(2.62)				(1.62)		(18.28)	(27.29)	(25.42)	(87,88)
Barmer	362302	14326	7629	78734	4315	12593	21172	–	722	181	501974
%	(72.17)	(2.85)	(1.52)	(15.63)	(0.86)	(2.51)	(4.23)		(0.14)	(0.14)	(17.82)
Bikaner	1368550	16570	–	–	31900	–	–	–	–	–	1417020
%	(96.58)	(1.17)			(2.25)						(49.12)
Jodhpur	412830	24470	121300	122390	–	–	–	–	–	–	680990
%	(60.46)	(3.58)	(18.03)	(17.93)	–	–	–	–	–	–	(30.79)
Churu	44844	6591	–	–	–	2084	853	–	2728	–	57100
%	(78.54)	(11.54)				(3.65)	(1.49)		(4.78)		(3.39)
Ganganagar	287378	14073	–	–	–	–	–	–	–	–	301451
%	(95.33)	(4.67)									(14.77)
Jhunjhunu	7292	–	–	6330	11231	–	–	–	71	–	24924
%	(29.25)			(25.40)	(45.06)				(0.29)		(4.20)
Sikar	10499	2000	5205	26453	6083	19627	–	–	1101	73	71041
%	(14.79)	(2.83)	(7.33)	(37.23)	(8.56)	(27.62)			(1.54)	(0.10)	(9.17)
Nagaur	8700	16500	–	–	–	20900	38500	–	–	–	84600
%	(10.28)	(19.5)				(24.70)	(45.52)				(4.78)
Pali	18473	7546	5250	46025	100364	–	–	–	180	360	178198
%	(10.37)	(2.24)	(2.95)	(25.83)	(56.34)				(0.10)	(0.17)	(14.49)
Jalore	10937	–	8297	9491	67248	–	–	–	–	806	96779
%	(11.30)		(9.57)	(9.75)	(69.55)					(0.83)	(9.15)
Total	3432120	197173	149481	289423	221141	114113	60525	64111	996762	925451	6448500
%	(53.21)	(3.05)	(2.32)	(4.49)	(3.43)	(1.77)	(0.94)	(1.00)	(15.45)	(14.34)	(100.00)

been evident that systematic photo interpretation enables to analyse and map the different areas of sand dunes according to their present land use. The main findings of the study of photo interpretation has been summarised in Table 2.3. Another important finding is given below (Sen, 1977).

Sand dunes in the north-western part of Nagaur district, south-eastern Bikaner and north-eastern Jodhpur are in general cultivated as indicated by the 'check board pattern' of the images in the photographs. Regional and photo-pattern clearly indicates the occurrence of dunes at different tiers or elevations. Stereoscopic study indicates the formation of terraces by the dunes. Terraces at 3 elevations in the west and even 4 in the east with narrow interdune lands can be easily identified by direct photo-analysis. Terraces are identified by sharp 'break' of slopes with alternate light tones. The check board and grid pattern and rapid tonal variation indicate that these dunes are cultivated since long back. Biotic interference including uncontrolled grazing resulted the wind blown sands to fill-up the interdune lands between the initial or original dunes resulting the terrace like formations. The alternate light and dark stipples of the images within the check board pattern along the dunes are noticed. Subsequent field checking reveals cropping of *bajra* by dry farming where the images have light stipple structure in the photographs. The dark stipples having diffused boundary constitute current fallow lands. Sample area analysis or field verification of the findings of the photo interpretation shows only 4 to 5 per cent changes of which 90 per cent are due to fresh development and only 10 per cent due to wrong interpretation.

Nomenclature of the Mapping Units for Sand Dunes

It has now been suggested that the stabilised dunes should not be mapped as sandy wastes, the level on which the land use class of a dune is to be determined should be based on the type of survey and the mapping scale. The detailed land use of the dunes should be cartographed only on 1:20,000 and above scale. For detailed reconnaissance survey and mapping following scheme is now being tentatively standardised and followed:

1. The dune areas along with narrow interdunal plains, if any, which can hardly be distinguished from dunes, should be demarcated on the base map.
2. The areas demarcated should be traversed systematically along some transacts in case of reconnaissance survey and on sample basis—following a grid—for detailed reconnaissance survey. The gross land use of the dunes are then to be studied. While the study is based merely on eye observation in case of reconnaissance mapping aided by "convergence of evidence" collected by local informations, the semi-detailed mapping should be based on detailed survey of the sample dunes. The type of land use exceeding 50 should determine the land use mapping unit of the dunes. The land use class such determined, should be projected for other dunes of similar occurrence and characteristics.

Examples

Figure 2.1 represents a dune fed tract of the Shergarh area in Jodhpur district. The intensity, degree and extent of the dunes here is very high—being 60 to 80 per cent of the area covered by white against dark background. Specific photo-pattern of the region is large area covering in a continuous manner often interrupted by hummocks (sand dunes) of varying sizes. The images are marked by contrasted tones. Sandy plains are best identified by medium grey tones. Sandy hills or dunes are identified by complex and unusual forms. Images of the dunes are often marked by stippled structure and coarse texture; size and shapes are irregular.

Based primarily on the interpretation of 5 landsat imageries, (1:1,000,000) supplied by ISRO a tentative land use map of Rajasthan has been prepared on 1:1,000,000. This is cartographed on the basis of tonal variation of the images aided by the study of "convergence of evidence". Ground truth of the areas, already surveyed by Basic Resources Studied Division of Central Arid Zone Research Institute, are also considered. No relationship between the images and its corresponding ground features are established to map the oran and the abadi areas. These, however, cannot be mapped on 1:1,000,000 scale. The map however has been found very useful to make the initial land use classification for

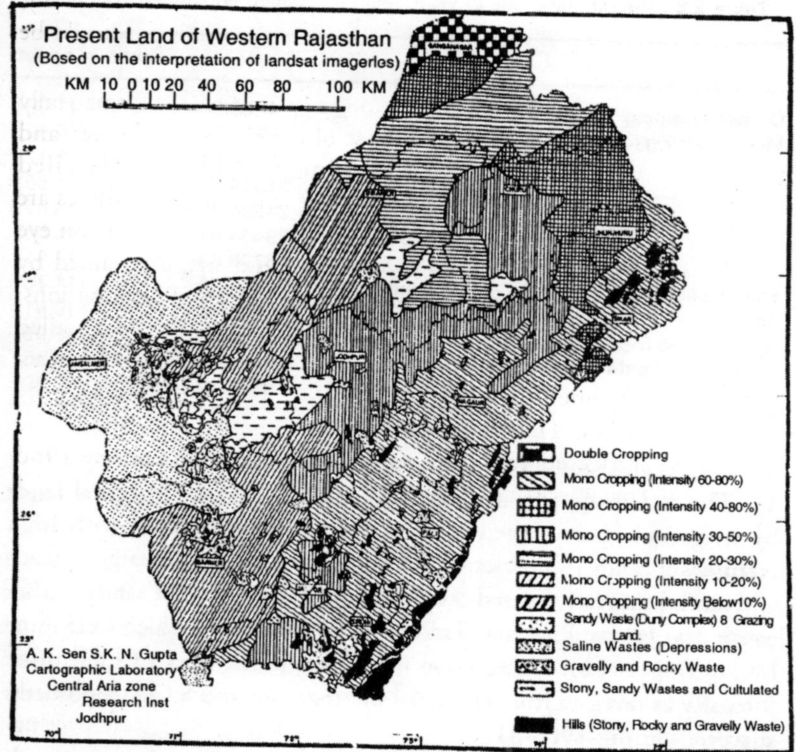

Fig. 2.1: Lard Use Map of W. Rajasthan based on the Interpretation of Landsat Imageries.

surveying further details and to pinpoint the problem areas. It is possible to find out and map only the areas having more than 100km^2. The mapping units established are shown in Table 2.3.

Uneconomic Land Use Practices and Overexploitation of Water Resources in Rajasthan Canal Project Area (Fig. 2.1)

Investigation on land use carried out in between 70°45' to 75°0' E and 29°30'N just to the south of the old Ghaggar river bed (in Hissar district of Haryana) and southern Ghaggar canal revealed some interesting feature.

The southern part of the region was waterlogged flanked by sandy

Table 2.3 : Present land use of W. Rajasthan (Based on landsat imageries)

		Areas in sq. km	
Double cropping		4268.88	(1.90)
Monocropping	(60-80%)	50776.74	(18.62)
"	(40-80%)	49874.92	(19.17)
"	(30-50%)	31562.71	(11.56)
"	(20-30%)	24895.45	(8.83)
"	(10-20%)	29404.55	(10.56)
"	Below 10 %	8798.63	(3.91)
Sandy waste (duny complex and grazing land)		26440.05	(11.76)
Saline		1802.41	(0.81)
Gravelly and rocky waste		11786.85	(5.09)
Stony, sandwaste and cultivated		9459.40	(4.56)
Hills		6637.19	(3.29)

hummocks and sand dunes as mapped by Survey of India during 1912-14. The reclamation of the waterlogged areas and the marginal lands by irrigation later converted them into cultivated lands with high intensity of 80 to 100 per cent. But the cultivation of the marginal lands and sand dunes have caused the shifting and deposition of sands further south near Jasana, Ramsara, Ratanpura, Rajkawra etc., which were dune free during 1912-14, and have now become the sites of high dune intensity as revealed from the aerial photographs and S.O.I. toposheets surveyed during 1960-61.

Recent survey (Sept. 1978) has shown further increase of sands throughout the area which is due to the indiscriminate cutting of the shrubs and trees. This has led to the deterioration of good agricultural lands and has increased the desertification intensity. The inundated areas which were waterlogged as early as in 1912 have become saline and this particular problem is gradually increasing towards the south in recent years.

The study thus sharply bring into focus the biotic interferences of the marginal lands which should be scientifically managed along with judicious exploitation of water resources.

3. The seepage problems along the canal irrigated areas have caused waterlogged areas in Suratgarh, Tibi, Hanumangarh, Anupgarh areas. This has increased the salinity hazards.

4. The overgrazing and cultivation of the sand dunes and the marginal lands in Bhadra, Nohar and Suratgarh tehsils has led to the shifting of sands in the adjacent Churu district. The district has recently shown a considerable increase of desert sand, sand drifts and the existing stabilised dunes, which have increased vertically and new sand dunes are developing round Churu, Tarenger tehsils.
5. The intensive and uneconomic irrigation has caused waterlogging problems and an area of about 20 sq. kms has been submerged near Suratgarh area.
6. The water-table has been considerably increased and has reached with 2' to 3' round Suratgarh, Borpal and Rangmahal areas. This has threatened the prehistoric excavation site at Rangmahal, Kalibangha, Hanumangarh and dry beds of Saraswati or Ghaggar, etc.

Recommendations

A. Sandy wastes

(i) Enclosure and complete stoppage of biotic activity for 10-15 years.
(ii) Mulching and trace plantation.
(iii) Seeding with suitable grass species.

B. Rocky, stony and gravelly wastes

(i) Detailed survey for exploration of minerals.
(ii) Providing diversion structure for diversion of run-off to desirable points.
(iii) Providing run-off collection points for collection of water for livestock and human consumption.
(iv) Providing recharge wells.

C. Saline waste

Detailed survey is needed to find out the possibilities of extracting salt for commercial purposes. Salt tolerant crops can be presented in the surrounding areas.

REFERENCES

Govt. of India — Ministry of Food and Agriculture and U.N.E.S.C.O. (1964). *Proc. Symp. on the Problems on Ind. Arid Zone*, Jodhpur.

Sen, A.K. (1972). "Land utilisation mapping to estimate the wastelands of arid zone in Rajasthan by photo interpretation technique". *Ind. Nat. Sc. Acad. Bull.* No. 44, pp. 67-71.

Sen, A.K. (1974). "Categorisation of land utilization units in arid zone". Dec. *Geog. XII* (1): 61-72.

Sen, A.K. (1977). "Aerial Photo Interpretation to analyse the land use pattern of sand dunes". *Geog. Rev. Ind.* 39(4) : 346-357.

3

Identification of the Wastelands

Hridai R. Yadav

Introduction

The term wasteland is not a new phenomena. It was used to indicate little common land usually on less fertile soil, which failed to field a return to the medieval farmers. A layman may define the wasteland which is lying uninhabited, uncultivated and left after use or land which is no longer serving any purpose. The adjective waste has now disappeared because in many cases these common lands are much valued as open spaces. Dudley Stamp gave an appropriate definition in this connection, "The wastelands may be defined as the land which has been previously used but which has been abandoned and for which no further use has been found."[1]

The Wastelands Survey and Reclamation Committee[2] has also defined, "The term wastelands as those lands which are either not available for cultivation or are left-out of cultivation without being cultivated like fallows and culturable waste". Thus, it embraces following types of waste lands :

(i) Land not available for cultivation, barren and uncultivable waste;

(ii) Other uncultivated land excluding fallows, culturable waste, permanent pastures and land under miscellaneous trees and crops; and

(iii) Fallows.

Thus, the above discussed Wasteland Survey and Reclamation Committee includes in the culturable waste all land available for cultivation but not taken up for cultivation or abandoned after a few years owing to some reason or the other. Such lands may be fallows for more than five years and may be covered with shrubs. Lands which are reserved for pasture for the grazing purposes are not included under culturble wastes. Fallows of one year are classified as current fallow and those of one to five years are classified as fallows other than current fallow.

Thus, the wastelands for the purpose of extension of cultivation are confined to other uncultivated land excluding fallows and fallows other than current fallow.[3]

Wastelands are those lands which are uncultivable or presently unutilized but have been used previously, which have been abandoned and no further use has been found due to some reason or the other.[4]

Definition

The wastelands definition which is used in this chapter to diagnose the wastelands is under :

> "Wastelands are those lands, which are uncultivable or presently lying unutilised due to different constraints but have been used previously which is giving very low actual return of its economic potential, which are ecologically unstable, or whose top soil has completely lost its fertility status, which have developed toxity for the growth of crops and trees due to environmental or anthropogenic problems have been abandoned and no further use have been found."

Wastelands Classification

There are five main land use categories and nine sub-classified land use categories as classified by the Directorate of Economics and Statistics of the Ministry of Agriculture[5], which are :

From these five main categories of land use three categories, *viz.*, land not available for cultivation, other uncultivated land excluding fallows and fallows are helpful in formulating wastelands classification. These categories are sub-divided from which only culturable waste and fallows other than current fallow are taken for the classification of wastelands. Two categories of land not available for cultivation, i.e., land put to non-agricultural use which cannot be categorised as wasteland because such lands are not used for agricultural practices, the barren and uncultivable lands which cannot be brought under cultivation because these lands are left permanently out of cultivation. The other uncultivated lands excluding fallows, permanent pastures and grazing grounds, land under miscellaneous trees are used for some or the other purposes but not for any agricultural uses, so these cannot be categorized as wastelands while from this category culturable wasteland has been taken for the classification of wastelands because :

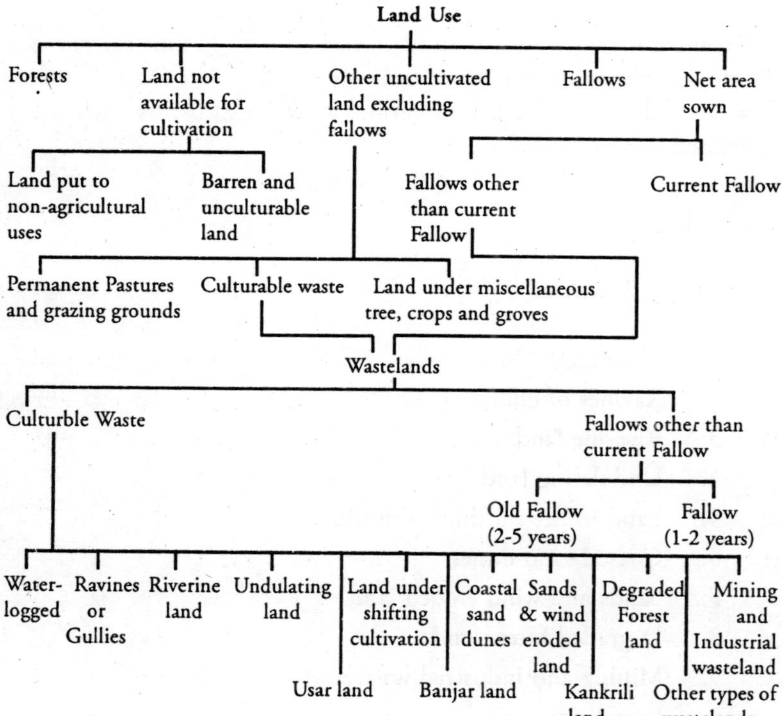

> "Culturable wastelands are those lands which are available for cultivation but not taken up for cultivation or abandoned after a few years for one reason or the other."

The current fallow is not considered for the further classification of wastelands because such lands are left fallow to maintain the fertility status of the soil and within a year same lands are recultivated but fallows other than current fallow are taken for the further classification of wastelands because:

> "The current fallows, within a year, are not brought back under cultivation due to some (environmental or anthropogenic) problems of the farmers, such lands are classified as fallows which are considered as the wastelands."

Excludng the above discussed seven categories from nine categories of land-use only culturable wasteland and fallows other than current fallow are taken for the classification of wastelands, as they are enumerated.

Wastelands

A. Culturable Wasteland

1. Waterlogged land
2. Ravines of gullies
3. Riverine land
4. Undulating land
5. Land under shifting cultivation
6. Coastal sand dunes
7. Sands and wind eroded land
8. Degraded forest land
9. Mining and industrial wasteland
10. Usar lands

11. Banjar lands
12. Kankrili lands
13. Other types of wasteland

B. Fallows other than Current Fallow

14. Old fallow (2-5 years)
15. Fallow (1-2 years)

The above classified different types of wastelands are defined and explained below :

Waterlogged Land

Waterlogged land is that land where the water-table is at or near the surface and water stands for most of the year and soil poses within the root zones of the crop get saturated with water which inhibits the growth and activity of plants due to these problems, such lands are left uncultivated.

Ravines or Gullies

Ravine means a system of gullies or gorges worn out by torrents of water and gullies running more or less parallel to each other and draining into a major river or its tributaries.

Riverine Land

Riverine land are the result of localised surface run-off affecting unconsolidated material causing undulating terrain through water erosion. Riverine is the initial stage of land dissection which leads to the development of gully and ravinous land.

Undulating Land

Undulating lands are those lands which are of the undulating nature prone to degradation.

Land under Shifting Cultivation

Those lands are included under shifting cultivation which are the result of trees and burning in forest areas for growing crops, thereby resulting in extensive soil losses leading to the land degradation.

Coastal Sand Dunes

Coastal sand dunes are those coastal areas which are affected by sand dunes through accumulation of sand *in situ* or transported by water erosion in coastal areas.

Sands and Wind Eroded Lands

Sands and wind eroded lands are those areas which have an accumulation of sand through wind erosion in the hot desert areas, *in situ* or transported in inland areas.

Degraded Forest Land

Degraded forest lands are those areas which are notified under the Forest Act in which denudation of vegetative cover results in such lands.

Mining and Industrial Wasteland

Mining wastelands are those lands where large-scale mining operations bring about the degradation of land and resultant mine dumps.

Industrial wastelands are those lands which are subject to degradation as a result of effects caused by large-scale industrial effluent discharges.

Usar Land

Those fluffy soils which have a whitish or greyish appearance and are deposited on the surface, which are not easily cultivable, are generally known as reh, or rehar or usar.

Banjar Land

Those lands which were taken up for cultivation but are presently out of cultivation for a period of not less than five years. These lands are left uncultivated for a very long period of time and such type of lands are called by villagers as Banjar land.

Kankrili Land

Areas where concretion takes place and Kankars are visible on the upper earth surface and sometimes at a certain depth, is called Kankrili. In many areas, the Kankars are exposed on the surface mainly bacuase of the removal of the top soil due to erosion.

Old Fallow Land

Old fallow lands are those lands which were under cultivation but presently are out of cultivation for a period of not less than two years and not more than five years.

Fallow Land

Those lands which would be taken up for cultivation but are temporarily out of cultivation for not less than one year and not more than two years are called fallow lands.

Other Types of Wastelands

Other types of wastelands include those lands which cannot, as predefinition be categorised into the above heads. This is primarily a class derived from the village handbook. The other types of wastelands are those lands which were under cultivation but presently are left out of cultivation due to some reason or the other.

Conclusion

Thus, the wastelands may be diagnosed and defined as those lands which are uncultivable or presently lying unutilised but have been used previously, which is giving very low return of its economic potential or whose soil has lost its fertility status, have been abandoned and no further use have been found.

From the land use categories culturable waste and fallows other than current fallow have been taken to classify the wastelands which are mainly Waterlogged, Ravines, Riverine, Undulating, Land under shifting cultivation, Coastal sand dunes, Sands and wind eroded land, Degraded forest land, Mining and Industrial wasteland, Usar lands, Banjar lands, Old fallow, Fallow, Kankrili and other types of wastelands.

Notes

1. Ministry of Food and Agriculture, Government of India, Wastelands Survery and Reclamation Committee, *Report on the Location and utilisation of Wastelands in India*, Part X, Uttar Pradesh, Delhi, 1961.
2. Stamp, L.D. "The land of Britain, Its use and Misuse", 1948. Vol XV, November, 1968, A.M.U.G.S., Aligarh.
3. Shafi, M., "Problems of Wastelands in India", *The Geographer*, Vol. XV, November, 1968, A.M.U.G.S., Aligarh.
4. Wasteland (Definition and Data Base), *Technical Task Group Report*, Submitted to National Wasteland Development Board, 1985, New Delhi.
5. Yadav, H.R., "Genesis and Utilization of Wastelands", 1986, Concept Publishing Co. Pvt. Ltd., New Delhi.

4

Problems and Prospects of Afforestation of Salt-affected Soils

H.S. Gill and *I.P. Abrol*

The natural resources of a nation *inter alia* are of paramount importance for the development of the economic and social life of its citizens. Generation and supply of basic necessities for this purpose require exploitation of these resources. This exploitation should be rational and needs maintenance of a proper balance between the biosphere and the physical environment and regulation of their utilization rate on a long-term basis as these resources could never be an unlimited entity of a country. Inevitably, this requires efficient planning and constant vigilance while monitoring exploitation of the natural resources.

Burgeoning population of India has resulted in overexploitation, misuse and mismanagement of the earth's most abundant natural resources: soil and forests. Expanding demands as a consequence of enormously increasing population have exerted a tremendous pressure on our land and the natural resources. It has been estimated (Swaminathan, 1980) that between 1951-52 and 1975-76 about 4.14 million ha of forest area was deforested in India alone (Table 4.1). Clearance of the forest area for agricultural use and river valley projects took over 60 per cent and 12 per cent of this total respectively. The rest was used for construction of roads, establishment of industries and other miscellaneous purposes. In the humid tropics of the Third World, about 7.5 million ha of forest area are being deforested annually to put the land under alternative uses (Lanly and Clement, 1979). According to the World Bank Sector Policy Paper on Forestry published in 1978, about half of the forest area in the developing countries was cleared for the agricultural use between 1900 and 1966. At the present levels of demand the remaining tropical forest will vanish in 60 to 80 years (Spears, 1979). This implies that indiscriminate deforestation for agricultural land use to produce food requirements is being followed at the cost of a agile and benevolent agro-ecological system in countries like ours. This trend would be dangerous for the future and is needed to be checked evolving viable alternative technologies. Thus, the most important task faced by the mankind today is to solve the problems of hunger and malnutrition by technologies that do not overburden non-renewable resources and that do not impoverish our natural resources *vis-à-vis* healthy ecological system.

Table 4.1: Forest Area Deforested for Different Purposes during 1951-52 to 1975-76

Purpose	*Area deforested*	
	Million ha	*Per cent of total*
River valley projects	0.48	11.6
Agricultural use	2.51	60.6
Road construction	0.06	1.5
Establishment of industries	0.13	3.1
Miscellaneous purposes	0.96	23.2
Total	**4.14**	**100.0**

Source: Swaminathan, M.S., 1980.

Why Afforestation?

General public awareness about afforestation in India is increasing rapidly. Tree plantations (a forest crop or stand raised artificially either by sowing or planting) are known for significant aid in economic development. Major benefits of plantation forestry include creation of resources to meet demand for wood and wood products; utilization of land unfit for viable agriculture; creation of employment in the rural areas; development of an infrastructure of roads, communication, services, houses, shops, schools often to remote areas and integration of tree planting with other land uses and the environmental role of the forests. The most striking benefit of raising plantations in tropical climates is rapid growth. In many parts, the tropical plantations were found to yield several times the amount of wood than from natural tropical forests and most forests in the temperate regions.

Furthermore, insurance of ecological security to sustain agricultural production in the long-term rests in our area under forests. Universally recognized minimal 33per cent of the total geographical area under forests coincides with the National Forest Policy of India enunciated long back on May 12, 1952, but its implementation has remained a tardy job. Multiplicity of development activities in other spheres and the requirement to produce more and more food alarmingly increasing population in the meantime has infatuated the forest cover to shrink further (Table 4.2). Besides the outstanding physical contribution of the trees and forests in the economic development of forest industry, their beneficial influence on the environment has a special significance. This influence help in stabilizing the soil (a vital natural resource), preventing erosion, controlling water run-off in the catchment areas, providing shelter from wind and heat and against dust and sandstorms. But despite these glaring benefits, the forest area of our country continues to be overexploited and is under constant pressure.

Since an overwhelming majority of Indians are rural inhabitants, the chief energy source for cooking food and for warmth in the country is the fuelwood. Present supply of the fuel and timber wood is exceedingly less than the demand. Therefore, illicit felling of the production forests and burning of a few million tonnes of nutrient elements in the form of dung cakes and other agricultural wastes of potential manurial value occur as a consequence of this mismatch. The fuelwood crisis is growing worldwide, as Eric Eckholem (*Natural History*, Oct. 1975) states in his article entitled "The firewood crisis", "the most profound ecological challenge of the twentieth century is growing demand and enough food to feed the world's population, there won't be enough firewood to cook it".

Afforestation, But Where?

The National Commission on Agriculture reviewing the situation in 1972 emphasized the extension of forest cover and considered several possibilities. Thus, due to increasing pressure on goods and productive soils for crop production, extension of forest area requires potentially arable lands presently lying barren (Table 4.2) to be afforestated. Much land, ill-suited to agriculture, is potentially available for forest plantations. Singh (1975) points that 13 per cent of the land area in India, about 43.6 million ha, is lying waste and much of it is suitable for plantation forestry. Land utilization Statistics of India (Table 4.2) indicate that most of the potentially arable land is already under cultivation. But a considerable hectarage not presently under cultivation but potentially arable has been lying barren due to one or another soil constraint and the lack of economic and proven technologies for their reclamation. The National Commission on Agriculture in its report estimated that approximately 40 million hectares were lying barren because of different constraints (Table 4.3) offered in their reclamation. A promising category among such barren lands drawing our attention is the salt-affected soils.

Table 4.2 : Land Utilization Statistics of India (1978-79).

Sl. No.	*Land use*	*Area*	
		Million ha	*Percentage to reporting area*
1.	Area under forests	67.44	22.1
2.	(i) Area under non-agricultural uses	39.30	12.9
		17.80	5.8
	(ii) Barren and unculturable land	21.50	7.1
3.	Other uncultivated land (excluding fallow land)	33.01	10.9
	(i) Permanent pastures and other grazing land	12.16	4.0
	(ii) Land under miscellaneous tree crops and grows not included in net sown area	3.91	1.3
	(iii) Culturable wasteland	16.95	5.6
4.	Fallow land	21.09	7.2
5.	Net sown area	142.94	46.9
6.	Total reporting area	304.68	100.0
7.	Total geographical area	328.78	—

Source: *Indian Agriculture in Brief*, 1982. Directorate of Economics and Statistics, Ministry of Agriculture and Co-operation, Govt. of India, New Delhi, p.8.

Table 4.3 : Approximate area and major constraints offered in the reclamation of potentially arable areas

Major Constraints	*Approximate area*	
	Million ha	*Percentage of total*
Waterlogging	6.0	15
Salinity and sodicity	7.0	18
Ravines	3.7	9
Laterite soils	12.0	30
Riverine lands, coastal sandy areas, stony and gravelly lands, high altitude and steeply sloping lands	11.3	28
Total	**40.0**	**100**

Source : National Commission on Agriculture; 1976. Ministry of Agriculture and Irrigation, Government of India, New Delhi.

Extent of Salt-Affected Soils

Salt affected soils are generally characterized as the soils that have been adversely modified for the growth of most plants by the action or presence of soluble salts, exchangeable sodium (ES) or both. Genesis of such involves accumulation of soluble salts in excess amounts, sometimes only temporarily. The possible source of the excess salts are one or more of the following (Abrol and Fireman, 1977):

(i) High salt deposits inherited to the soil from original parent material during soil formation,

(ii) Salts contained in the irrigation water applied or lost in conveyance through irrigation distribution systems,

(iii) More salts in water inflows (seepage) from upslope, and

(iv) Salts from upward movement (capillary action) of water from groundwaters close to the soil surface. (Fig. 4.1)

It has been estimated that about 7 million ha of India's land occupy salt-affected soils (Abrol and Bhumbla, 1971). The principal constraints that reduce the productivity of such soils are soil salinity and sodicity. Most of the salt affected soils are generally associated with semi arid and arid climates. Based on the nature of the soil problem and their geographical distribution, salt affected soils occurring in the country can be broadly grouped as given in Table 4.4.

Table 4.4 : Distribution of salt-affected soils in India

Broad Group	*States in which the soils occur*	*Approximate area (M.ha)*
1. Coastal salt-affected soils		
(a) Coastal salt-affected soils	Gujarat	0.714
(b) Deltaic coastal salt-affected soils in the humid regions	W. Bengal, Orissa, Andhra . Pradesh and Tamil Nadu	1.394
(c) Acidic salt-affected soils	Kerala	0.016
2. Salt-affected soils of the medium and deep black soil regions	Karnataka, Madhya Pradesh Andhra Pradesh and Maharashtra	1.420
3. Salt-affected soils of the arid and semi-arid regions	Gujarat, Rajasthan Punjab, Haryana and Uttar Pradesh	1.000
4. Alkali soils of the Indo-Gangetic plains	Haryana, Punjab, Uttar Pradesh, Bihar, Rajasthan and Madhya Pradesh	2.500
Total area under salt-affected soils		7.044

Source : Abrol and Bhumbla, 1971 and Bhumbla, 1977.

These are only estimates and as remarked by Kanwar (1977), the magnitude of the problem is much more severe because an additional 20 million ha in the canal irrigated areas already run the risk of being degraded through the influence of salts. Differences in climate, soil characteristics including the nature of salts, available water resources and related features require a different approach for afforestation programmes of such soils occurring in different regions.

Identification of a Salt-Affected Soil

Physico-chemical properties of salt-affected soils reflect the amount and type of the salts present. This is best evaluated by the analysis of soil water under field conditions though it is seldom convenient. Therefore, a soil sample is tested under laboratory conditions. The standard laboratory procedure involves saturation of a soil sample with distilled water and then equilibration for a specified time period before extracting the moisture, called saturation extract, from the soil with vacuum filtration. Saturation extract is chemically analysed for pH, electrical conductivity, nature and amount of soluble cations (calcium, magnesium, potassium and sodium) and anions (carbonate, bicarbonate, chloride and sulphate). Thus, composition of the saturation extract and relative proportion of exchangeable cations determined by soil analysis is used to differentiate different types of salt-affected soils. The principal criteria used to identify the dominant constraint among the salt-affected soils are: (i) salinity of the saturation extract as measured by the electrical conductivity (EC_e) at 25°C; (ii) exchangeable sodium percentage and (iii) pH of the saturated soil paste. Thus, salt-affected soils are broadly classified into two groups: (i) Saline and (ii) Alkali soils. The basic characteristics of the two groups are presented in Table 4.5.

Table 4.5 : Salient characteristics of saline and alkali soils

Characteristic	*Saline soils*	*Alkali soils*
EC_e at 25°C (dsm^{-1})	4.0 or more	Generally less than 4.0
ESP	Variable	15 or more
pH (saturated soil paste)	Less than 8.2	8.2 or more
Chemistry of soil solution	Dominated by chloride and sulphate ions	Dominated mainly by carbonate or bicarbonate anions or both
Effect of electrolytes on soil particles	Flocculation	Dispersion
Main adverse (toxic) effects on plants	High osmotic pressure of soil solution	Alkalinity of soil solution
Geographical distribution	Associated mainly with arid and semi-arid areas	Associated mainly with semi-arid and sub-humid area
First aim of reclamation	Removal of excess electrolytes through leaching	Lowering or neutralizing the high pH through chemical amelioration

Saline Soils

Saline soils are defined by the presence of excess of soluble salts with neutral reaction. An electrical conductivity of the soil saturation extract of about 4 milli mhos per cm is generally taken as dividing limit between the saline and the non-saline soils. The dominant soluble salts in saline soils mostly comprise chlorides and sulphates of sodium, calcium and magnesium.

Sometimes, saline soils contain appreciable amounts of nitrates but only rarely. In highly saline soils, salts of sodium dominate. Because of the neutral reaction of these salts, saline soils never have a high pH value and when measured on a saturated soil paste, it is always less than 8.2. Presence of excess soluble salts induce flocculation of the clay fraction and for this reason the physical properties of saline soils are generally good. Sometimes, when the groundwater-table is near to the soil surface, the physical properties may not be favourable for growth of all the plants. Plant growth in saline soils is impaired chiefly due to the osmotic effects of excess soluble salts. Accumulation of specific ions like boron, chlorine and sodium in plants in toxic levels may often affect plant growth adversely.

Alkali Soils

In contrast to saline soils, alkali soils are those which adversely affect plant growth due to excessive amount of the element sodium on the exchange complex of the soil. An exchangeable sodium percentage (ESP) of about 15 is generally considered as the upper limit between the normal and the alkali soils. Alkali soils always have measurable to appreciable amounts of highly alkali salt, sodium carbonate. Presence of sodium carbonate imparts to these soils high pH value. An ESP of 15 is always associated with a saturation paste pH of about 8.2. The adverse effect of exchangeable sodium on plant growth is mainly associated with its adverse effect on the physical properties of the soil. High ESP causes dispersion of the soil colloids which in turn result in blocking of the soil pores. Consequently, air and water movement is impeded. Applied irrigation or rainwater tend to stagnate, creating unfavourable conditions for plant roots to respire and absorb water and nutrient elements smoothly. Plant growth in alkali soils may also be checked due to the accumulation of toxic quantities of elements like sodium or a deficiency of other essential plant nutrients like calcium and zinc which are not in forms easily available to plants due to high pH of such soils. Many alkali soils have pH values as high as 10.6. Presence of compact and difficult to penetrate calcic horizon (calcium carbonate concretions) in alkali soils is yet another growth limiting characteristic. This layer acts as a barrier and offers severe mechanical impedance to the downward growth of roots and of the movement of water and air within the soil profile. In scientific literature alkali soils have also been commonly called sodic soils, because these soils have high amounts of exchangeable sodium.

Afforestation of Salt-Affected Soils

About 40 per cent of the barren salt-affected soils of India are confined to the Indo-Gangetic plains in the states of Uttar Pradesh, Haryana and Punjab and high soil sodicity (alkali soils) is reported (Abrol and Bhumbla, 1971) to be the major constraint impairing their productivity. Since these soils have formed under the influence of sodium carbonate, its hydrolysis imparts high pH and high ESP which in turn has an adverse effect on the physico-chemical and the biological conditions of soils. In addition, presence of hard *kankar pan* (calcic horizon) around one metre depth is another severe barrier that hinders root development. Proprietary rights of a sizable chunk of these soils in the given three states mostly lie with the village Panchayats (judicial village bodies). Afforestation of such land, thereby, suits better for the promotion of social and farm forestry. This would also help having a healthy agro-ecological system of the region known for its higher food production capacity in the country.

Considering a vast scope for raising tree crops on such soils, available research information is inadequate. A careful review of most of the past researches on the afforestation (establishment of trees on bare or grassland having no forest for at least 50 years) of salt-affected soils indicates that a few tree species can be grown successfully in highly sodic soils by adopting appropriate management practices. But lack of systematic experimental evidences concerning adaptability and tolerance of the species to varying degrees of soil sodicity impair successful planning and planting operations. In several of the investigations in India and abroad, tree species were found greatly differing in their tolerance to soil salinity and sodicity conditions. But actual data concerning soils on which these were grown are mostly lacking. Therefore, a critical evaluation of the tolerance limits can never be made. Moreover, suitability of a forest tree species is also to be decided in respect to the local operations and other soil factors.

Tree Planting in Sodic Soils

In the early sixties, it was suggested (Khan and Yadav, 1962), the successful afforestation of salt-affected soils has rather limited prospects unless the soil conditions are ameliorated to a desired level by adopting appropriate techniques. Forest departments of Uttar Pradesh, Haryana and Punjab made several attempts to plant trees on such soils but without much success. But later it was suggested (Pande, 1967) that the soils can be afforestated using replacement technique which involves replacement of soil from a pit with 90 cm each of depth and diameter by normal soil from another site of good and productive soil. But Yadav *et al.* (1972) concluded while studying suitability of a few tree species in a highly sodic soil (pH 10.0) that saplings planted in pits refilled with a mixture of original sodic soil. Fifty per cent GR (gypsum requirement) and 24 kg FYM, were on a par with the good soil for growth and survival percentage. Recently, Sandhu and Abrol (1981) reported a new technique, an augerhole method for planting tree species.

In the case of tree species, because of their deep-root systems, management of root zone by modifying the soil environment with a limited quantity of gypsum in he profile to a deeper depth may play a vital role than using soil amendments to ameliorate a few centimeters of surface soil adopted for most of the crop plants. Acting on this principle, therefore, comprehensive field scale experimentation is being executed at the Central Soil Salinity Research Institute, Karnal, to evaluate selected tree species for their tolerance to soil sodicity and mechanical impedance and improvement in planting techniques over the existing ones which are comparatively uneconomical and pesky.

To evaluate relative tolerance and growth response of *Eucalyptus tereticornis* Sm. and *Acacia nilotica* (L.) Willd. ex. Del. (Babul) to selected methods of site preparation for their plantation in highly alkali soils (Table 4.6), two field experiments are in progress at the Central Soil

Salinity Research Institute Farm near village Gudha of Karnal district (Haryana). In one experiment, pit method of tree planting was compared with the planting of given species in augerholes of varying dimensions (diameter × depth) whereas effect of different filling mixtures used to refill the augerholes of constant dimensions (15 cm × 120 cm) on their survival and growth was studied in another. Results (Table 4.7) indicate that survival of both, Acacia and Eucalyptus, remained about cent per cent in all the augerholes of varying dimensions and pit throughout their growth of 48 months. However, notable differences were effected within various filling mixtures used to refill the augerholes. Similar observations were made regarding growth parameters, namely, height and girth diameter at one metre height from the soil surface.

Data further indicate that mixing of gypsum alone either 3 kg or 6 kg with original soil (OS) significantly improved the penultimate survival of Eucalyptus although it was inferior to the mixture of gypsum and 8 kg FYM with OS or sand. This indicated beneficial interaction of gypsum and FYM for Eucalyptus. In Acacia, gypsum levels and its combination with FYM and sand did not differ much. This demonstrates relatively higher tolerance of Acacia to sodicity hazard of soil. Results also conclude success of augerhole technique which is economical and less troublesome than the pit method generally recommended for alkali soils. Further efforts are being made to fabricate tractor-operated auger that may dig augerholes mechanically making the task of preparing augerholes easy and less laborious.

Table 4.6: Soil characteristics of the experimental field

Profile depth (CM)	*pH**	*Ecx10³ dsm⁻¹*	*$CaCO_3$ (%) 2 mm*	*Concre-tions (%) (V/V) (%)*	*ESP %*	*Sand %*	*Silt %*	*Clay*
0-15	10.4	4.24	1.12	0.5	97	56	27	16
16-27	10.1	1.64	0.52	2.3	97	49	33	18
28-46	10.1	1.12	0.60	3.6	98	40	32	21
47-87	10.0	1.12	0.86	5.7	98	56	21	22
88-139	10.0	1.07	6.38	32.8	94	50	26	17
140-200	9.8	0.70	9.75	7.5	72	63	16	11

* Measured in 1 : 2 soil water suspension.

Girth growth of the Eucalyptus planted in augerholes of varying dimensions and pit was markedly higher than Acacia after 24 months of planting. But subsequently growth increments in Acacia were seen (Gill, Abrol and Sandhu, 1985) higher than Eucalyptus and differences were levelled off at 36 months growth stage and Acacia established marginal superiority after 48 months of planting. It is evident from Table 4.7 that the percentage increase in girth growth of Acacia is 3-4 times more than Eucalyptus until 48 months of growth over the initial 24 months of girth growth. Further, crown growth of Acacia is more encouraging than that of Eucalyptus. To maintain proper balance between the crown and the boll, horizontal growth of undesirable shoots on Acacia trunks were lopped after 16 and 41 months of planting. Moisture content on air-dry-weight basis of the air dried Acacia branches of potential fuelwood value ranged 25 to 30 per cent. Fuelwood yield (Table 4.8) in the pit treatment was higher than in the augerhole technique. Within different augerhole filling mixtures, mixture of gypsum and FYM with sand or OS were on a par but yielded significantly more fuelwood than the use of gypsum alone either 3 or 6 kg.

In another experiment it was found that *Casuarina equisetifolia* (L.) holds a promise for afforestation of alkali soils (Gill and Abrol, 1984). Its per cent survival stood cent per cent after 15 months of planting in augerholes refilled with original alkali soil. But mixing of gypsum alone or in conjunction with FYM resulted insignificantly more height growth (Fig. 4.1) than the OS treatment and its mixture with FYM. Other species which performed very well include *Prosopis juliflora* (Sw.) DC (Mesquite bean). It accumulated significantly higher biomass (Table 4.9) than other species tried. Species that performed only fairly include *Albizzia lebbec* (L.) Benth. (Siris) and *Azadirachta indica Juss* (Neem). Growth of *Syzygium fructicosum* DC (Jamoa) and *Dalbergia sissoo* Roxb (Shisham) was not normal although per cent survival of the latter species remained 100 even after 24 months of planting. Species which failed to grow include *Populus deltoides* Bartr. (Popular), *Morus indica* var *alba* (L.) (Shahtoot) and *Syzygium cuminii Wall* (Jamun).

Table 4.7: Effect of site preparation method and filing mixtures on the performance of given tree species in a highly alkali soil

Augerhole/pit dimensions	*Eucalyptus tereticornis Sm.*			*Per cent increase in girth over past 24 months*	*Acacia nilotica Willd-ex del*			*Per cent increase in girth over past 24 months*
	Survival %	*Height (m)*	*Girth circumference (mm)*		*Survival %*	*Height (m)*	*Girth circumference (mm)*	
Expt. I								
10 × 120 (T_1)	100	6.80	290	51	100	6.23	322	79
10 × 180 (T_2)	100	7.63	345	48	100	6.22	347	124
15 × 120 (T_3)	100	7.27	326	59	100	6.67	347	125
15 × 180 (T_4)	88	8.30	372	47	100	6.64	377	128
90 × 90 (T_5)	100	7.93	350	54	100	7.10	414	144
LSD (0.05)	NS	NS	—	NS	NS	NS	NS	—
Filling Mixtures				**Expt. II**				
OS (M_1)	0	—	—	51	6	5.84	150	—
OS + 3kg Gyp. (M_2)	32	4.31	168	51	94	5.48	295	269
SO + 3kg Gyp.+ 8kg FYM(M_4)	81	6.85	362	97	88	5.91	354	250
OS + 6kg Gyp. (M_3)	66	5.34	226	95	100	5.49	312	239
OS + 3kg Gyp.+ Sand (M_5)	88	7.94	366	79	100	5.81	389	238
LSD(0.05)	40	1.69	96	—	22	NS	NS	—

Table 4.8 : Fuelwood (t/ha) yielded by lopping branches on boll of Acacia

Treatment	*Time of lopping, months past planting*		
	16	*41*	*Total*
T_1	2.21	4.79	7.00
T_2	2.54	5.98	8.52
T_3	2.67	4.66	7.33
T_4	3.05	6.01	9.06
T_5	4.07	6.57	10.61
LSD (0.05)	1.00	NS	NS
M_1	0.00	0.78	0.78
M_2	1.08	4.96	6.04
M_3	1.28	5.12	6.40
M_4	1.83	7.07	8.90
M_5	2.48	7.15	9.63
LSD (0.05)	1.05	1.90	2.31

Source: Gill, Abrol and Sandhu (1985).

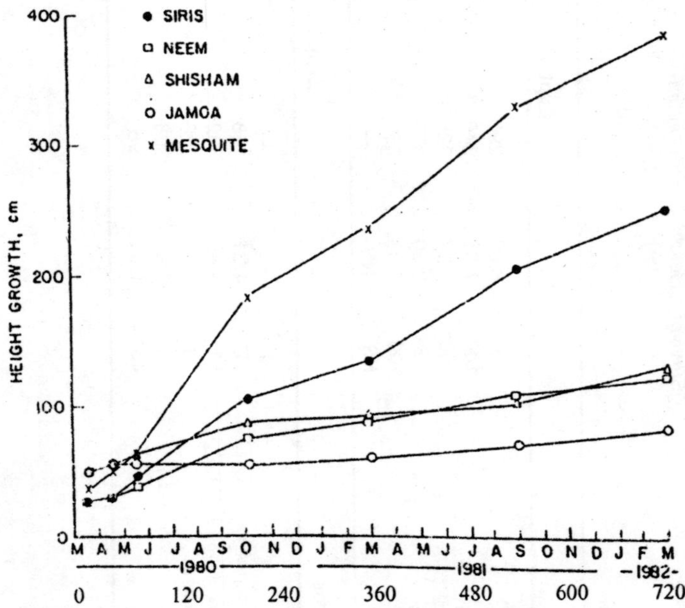

Fig. 4.1 : Growth Period, Days Past Planting Periodic height growth of selected species in respect of pothole depths.

Table 4.9: Performance of selected tree species in a highly sodic soil

Species	*Survival %*	*Height m*	*Dry matter g*	
			Roof	*Sheet*
Populus deltodis Bartr. *(Poplar)*	0	–	–	–
Morus indica cv alba Linn. *(Shahtoot)*	0	–	–	–
Syzygium cuminii Wall. *(Jamun)*	0	–	–	–
Syzygium fructicosum DC *(Jamoa)*	50	0.73	254	260
Azadirachta indica Juss. *(Neem)*	63	1.09	118	266
Albizzia lebbec Benth. *(Siris)*	69	2.08	1775	3044
Prosopis juliflora (SW) DC *(Mesquite)*	88	3.30	2662	11908
Dalbergia sisso Roxb. *(Shisham)*	100	1.06	149	165

Alkali or sodic soils are poorly permeable and allow very little rainwater to infiltrate. This causes loss of excellent quality rainwater from the area. Large amounts of run-off also erode huge amounts of nutrients-rich surface soil. Since many research findings indicate that tree plantations help in soil and water conservation, therefore, afforestation of sodic soils may be a useful practice on this account as well. Table 4.10 shows that for a return period of 2.33 and 5 years maximum rainfall occurring for one to five days varies between 12.0 and 24.1 cm. The maximum dry spell in the monsoon season for the same return period may vary between 28 and 34 days. Thus, areas where ensured irrigation is a limitation for successful cultivation of agricultural crops, growing trees which are deep-rooted and can meet their water requirement from the deeper horizons helps in overcoming drought conditions more easily. In view of this possibility, planting of tree species in furrow-trench system was tested in both saline and alkali soils and found effective in conserving rainwater successfully and in amelioration of the salt-affected soils.

Table 4.10: Maximum storm rainfall (mm) and dry spells for different return periods

Particular	*Return periods (years)*					
	1.01	*2.33*	*5*	*10*	*25*	*100*
Maximum one day rainfall	41	120	152	183	221	289
Maximum two days rainfall	51	155	201	238	285	355
Maximum three days rainfall	61	171	219	258	307	381
Maximum four days rainfall	67	179	228	268	318	394
Maximum dry spell in monsoon (days)	15	28	34	39	45	54

Scurce: Narayana *et al.* (1978).

Planting Trees in Saline Soils

Amelioration of saline soils involves leaching of soluble salts from the active root zone with good quality irrigation or rainwater. But in India such soils occur generally in areas where good quality water is not easily available and the underground water is mostly unsafe to use because of

Table 4.11: Tree species and their relative tolerance to soil salinity

Sr. No.	*Botanical name*	*English/common name*
	A. Highly Tolerant	
1.	*Tamarix articulata* Vahl.	Athel tarmarisk, farash
2.	*Tamarix gallica* L.	Tamarisk, farash
3.	*Casuarina cunninghamiana* Mig.	River oak, srub she-oak, Casuarina
4.	*Casuarina eqisetifolia* L.	Australian Pine, beef-wood tree, Jartor
5.	*Prosopis juliflora* (SW.) DC.	Mesquite bean
6.	*Acacia nilotica* (L.) Willdex Del.	Babul, kikar *desi*
7.	*Acacia deccurrens mollis* Wall.	Green and silver wattle
8.	*Acacia catechu* Willd.	Khair, jerusalem thorn
9.	*Zizyphus jujube* Lamk.	Ber, kool and Chinese date
10.	*Zizyphus spina-vulgaris* Will.	Christs thorn and nubk tree
11.	*Butea monosperma* (Lamk.) Taub.	Palas, dhak, flame of forest
12.	*Ailanthus excelsa* Roxb.	Maharuk, Tree of Heaven
13.	*Terminalia arjuna* Wight et Arn.	Arjun Tree, Kaku
14.	*Capparis aphylla* Roth.	Ker, kerro, kureal
	B. Moderately Tolerant	
1.	*Acacia cyanophylla* Willd.	Blue wattle
2.	*Acacia deccurrens dealbata* Link	Black and silver wattle
3.	*Parkinsonia aculeata* L.	Parkinsonia, Horse bean
4.	*Eucalyptus cameldulensis* Dehn.	River red gum, green gum
5.	*Eucalyptus citridora* Hook.	Tree lemon, citron scented gum
6.	*Eucalyptus tereticornis* Son	Blue gum, bastard box
7.	*Azadirachta indica* Juss.	Neem
8.	*Albizzia lebbec* (L.) Benth.	Siris
9.	*Dalbergia sisso* Roxb.	Shisham, sisoo, tahali
10.	*Leucaena leucocephala* (Lamk.) de Wit.	Ipil-ipil, Subabul.
11.	*Bauthinia alva var. Candida* L.	Bull hoof tree, kahnar
12.	*Populus euphratica* L.	Poplar, willows
13.	*Pinus halepensis* Mill.	Aleppo fir, Jerusalem pine

Source: Abrol and Gill (1983).

its high soluble salts content. In many soils where the monsoon rains result in sufficient leaching of the soluble salts but there high water-table becomes another problem that subsequently also causes salinity development. But, where the water-table is not a problem and soils are light textured, even highly saline waters can be used for the successful growth of tree plantations (Gill *et al.*, 1986). Thus, depending upon local resources and climate, selection of a suitable tree species and suitable planting method is of importance in saline soils.

A comprehensive list of tree species for their relative tolerance (Table 4.11) to salinity hazard of soil (Abrol and Gill, 1983) is presented. In saline soils, planning of tree species on raised beds is generally preferable when the water-table is near to the surface. This provides an additional soils space for the growth of roots. Choice of the tree species is the most important factor while afforestating saline soils though the management practices have their significant role in successful growth. Data are inadequate to generalize and demarcate tree species for specific conditions of soil salinity, however, on the basis of their relative performance, and a few systematic studies (Table 4.11) will help considerably.

REFERENCES

Abrol, I.P. and Bhumbla, D.R. (1971). Paper presented at FAO/UNDP Seminar on Soil Survey and Soil Fertility Research, Feb. 15-20, 1971, New Delhi, FAO, *World Soil Resources Report No. 41,* 42-51.

Abrol, I.P. and Fireman, M. (1977). Alkali and saline soils identification and improvement for crop production, C.S.S.R. I., Karnal, *Bulletin No. 4,* p. 32.

Abrol, I.P. and Gill, H.S. (1983). Grow trees where grains can't, *Farmer's Journal* 2(10), 40-45.

Bhumbla, D.R. (1977). In *Proceedings,* Indo Hungarian Seminar, Management of Salt Affected Soils, pp. 14-19, Central Soil Salinity Research Institute, Karnal.

Gill, H.S. and Abrol, I.P. (1984). A promise for sodic soils, *Intensive Agriculture* 21 (3), 5-6

Gill, H.S., Abrol, I.P. and Sandhu, S.S. (1985). Acacia excels Eucalyptus in alkali soils, *Indian Fmg.*, Feb., 1985 (accepted).

Gill, H.S., Rao, K.V.G.K. and Abrol, I.P. (1986). Growing tree plantations with saline water (in preparation).

Kanwar, J.S. (1977). *Soil Bulletin* 34, FAO, Rome.

Khan, W.A.W. and Yadav, J.S.P. (1962). Characteristics and afforestation problems of saline alkali soils. *Indian For.*, 83 (4), 259-271.

Lanly, J.P. and Clement, J. (1979). Present and future national forest and plantation areas in the tropics, *Unasylva* 123, 12-20.

Narayana, V.V.D., Gupta, S.K. and Tiwari, A.K. (1978). Rainfall and run-off analysis for rainwater management in agriculture: *Proceedings*. Symp. Hydrology of rivers with small and medium catchments, Vol. II, pp. 43-53.

Pande, G.C. (1967). Afforestation of Usar lands. *Proceedings*, 11th All Silviculturist Conference. Forest Research Institute, Dehra Dun.

Sandhu, S.S. and Abrol, I.P. (1981). Growth responses of *Eucalyptus tereticornis* and *Acacia nilotica* to selected cultural treatments in a highly sodic soil, *Indian J. Agric. Sci.* 51, 437-443.

Singly B. (1975). Role of forestry in mitigating the energy crisis in India, *Indian Forester* 101, 589-596.

Spears, J.S. (1979). Can the wet tropical forest survive? *Commonwealth For. Rev.* 58, 165-180.

Swaminathan, M.S. (1980). Indian Forestry at the crossroads. *International Tree Crops Journal* 1, 161-67.

Yadav, J.S.P., Bhumbla, D.R. and Sharma, O.P. (1972). Performance of certain forest species in a saline sodic soil; *Proceedings*. Symp. New Developments in the field of Salt Affected Soils. International Soc. Soil Sci., Cairo (1975), pp. 683-690.

5

An Approach to Wasteland Development

Arun Chavan

In this chapter I propose to deal with the problem of wasteland development with particular reference to Sangli district, where our group has been active for the last 17 years. With regard to land use pattern, geographical and social conditions Sangli has features which are common to western Maharashtra region. It comprises districts, excluding the three straddling the Western Ghats. The contents of the chapter therefore can be regarded as broadly applicable to this entire region.

In the extreme western corner of the district, the annual rainfall is up to 6,000 mm. In the eastern part it is as little as 400 mm. According to official statistics, of the total geographical area 62.25 per cent is chronically drought prone, having scanty and erratic rainfall. The features of the district's land use pattern for our present purposes are as mentioned below:

(i)	Total geographical area	861,000 ha
(ii)	Forest	47,700 ha
(iii)	Wasteland	1,41,000 ha

The environmental predicament of the district is flood-lit by the state of forest areas. The total forest area constitutes only 5.55 per cent of the total geographical area. The Forest Department owns 27,356 hectares of them and 20,391 hectares belong to the Revenue

Department. According to the Regional Plan document only 2,000 hectares have actual forest cover, which is further sub-divided into 725 hectares of protected forest and 1,275 hectares of "tree forest", which apparently is open for commercial exploitation. The development plan being prepared by the local Forest Sub-Division will cover 27,000 hectares. It proposes to implement the plant over a 20-year period. In 1985-86, the Department planted 1,093 hectares, spending Rs. 80.56 lakhs, of which Rs. 15 lakhs went for meeting the wage bill. The latter amount presumably does not include the cost of the Forest establishment. In 1986-87, the Department has to plant 657 hectares. It has moved for the transfer of the Revenue Forest land to itself, which has remained all these years unprotected and undeveloped.

The officially ordained compartmentalization of the publically owned non-agricultural land into wasteland, revenue, forest and Forest Department-controlled forest should forth with be abolished. Voluntary agencies concerned about ecology should be accepted as equal partners in eco-building activity and encouraged to take up chunks of these areas for reforestation. An unreserved appreciation of the practical advantage in promoting such a partnership is what is needed. An official reforestation programme tends to be a tree plantation exercise, in which species only of commercial utility and non-edible types are preferred. By the very nature of its implementation, the programme becomes capital-intensive. A reforestation programme has to become an eco-restoration programme, where, taking the cue from nature itself, growth of all kinds of trees, shrubs and vegetation should be promoted. Though, a universally acknowledged truth it needs vehement and repeated reiteration due to the curious propensities inherent in contemporary Indian reality. A great leeway has to be made up in double quick time without creating unmeetable demands on scarce financial resources. The best way to do so is to make the programme participatory. To ensure people's participation wasteland development should become a part and parcel of a programme for human development.

I wish to share with you all the experiences of our group in wasteland development.

We have identified 1,200 hectares of degraded lands from two development blocks, which belong to the State Departments of Revenue and Forest. We have collected socio-economic data about the communities which inhabit the eco-shade of the project. A population of 33,000 settled in 22 villages and smaller hamlets within the eco-shade have 15,000 head of ruminant cattle. They have 8,000 hectares under cultivation. We have identified 36 young persons from the villages who can develop into activists. Through the methods of group learning we expose them to various aspects of community development. When the project gets going there will be intensive training workshops where topics such as rational cropping patterns, livestock management, water harvesting, social health, sanitation, etc., will be dealt with.

Causes of Drought

The people of the area have long been suffering due to droughts. Recently, a workshop of the core group was held to study the situation and to determine the causes of drought. There was a broad agreement within the group that the lack of tree cover in the district was an important cause of repeated droughts, soil erosion and all the attendant ill-effects. The group was ready to lend its services in the task of tree plantation. It was sure that the people would participate in the programme if their economic well-being also could be assured. The group was able to see that environmental degradation has progressed parallelly with the economic down-sliding of the eco-shade fraternity. It felt that a comprehensive approach is called for, which revives the organic relationship of man with the milieu and enriches one with the genius of the other. It agreed that reforestation should be a human-oriented and free-hand replication of nature's design, that it would be suicidal to allow it to become an engineered animation of a blueprint for wood-based industry.

The programme ideas evolved by the core group are to be presented to the villages, which will be done when the project receives approval. The core group has thought of the machinery for project implementation. Each village will have a Project Implementation Committee (PIC). It will have representation for the village Panchayat, the school, the cooperatives. The Village Health Worker, the Gram Sevak, a female member of the Panchayat will be included in the PIC. The function of the PIC will be:

(i) Dissemination of project information and explaining the project's relation with the lives of the people.

(ii) Coordinating the developmental programmes.

(iii) Organizing Shramadan teams on the basis of one man-day per family per week.

(iv) Protection of the forested areas.

(v) Mobilizing greater participation in the official welfare and developmental programmes.

The core group was uneasy about the short-term deprival of usufruct to the eco-shade people. It, therefore, studied the quantum and quality of available usufruct of the project area. It found that the degraded area yielded a meagre benefit to 30 per cent of the population by way of cattle grazing. The number of households which depended on the area for fuel gathering was 10 per cent. They got a per-capita average of 7 kg of fuel at the end of a day's trek of the far-flung corners of the wasteland. Everyone concerned seemed to be aware that it was a diminishing source. Yet there would be no quick recompense to offer. Between the immediate loss of usufruct of whatever worth and the prospect of sumptuous long-term benefits there fell a chasm which needed to be bridged. Therefore, those having a house and few head of cattle have to be persuaded to go in for *gobargas* plants. Universalization of the smokeless *choola* is the other means to reduce the need for fuelwood. Seven villages have taken a lead in the matter and our animators have helped instal 406 smokeless *choolas* for which the householders themselves have invested. After the actual tree plantation starts three to four years have to elapse before the planted area yields fuel in the form of twigs, etc. To tide over this period, community fuel banks will have to be set up to cater to the needs of the hard-up households.

The second constraint is about fodder. To be able to ensure the cattle grazers willing cooperation community fodder banks will be needed to tide over the interregnum of two years. The reforested areas as well as other suitable areas will be used to produce richer varieties of grasses. A programme of livestock upgradation is proposed to be synchronized with the availability of fodder which will be sold to the livestock owners at the reduced rates. The underlying understanding would be that they should in turn sell a part of the increased milk yield at break even rate. It will be utilized to raise the nutritional status, especially of the children and mothers whose households do not have their own milk supply. Fodder distribution, milk procurement and distribution will be the responsibility of the PIC.

Basic Requirements

According to the thinking of the core group our wasteland development project will have to acquire the dimensions of a comprehensive eco-shade development project, whose salient features could be briefly stated as follows:

(i) *Skills Training*

(a) Horticultural and forest nurseries, to be owned and managed by young people as an income generating activity.

(b) Horticultural development.

(c) Tusser silk production.

(d) Bee keeping

(e) Fodder production and processing.

(f) Wood based crafts.

(ii) *Forestry*

(a) Survey and preparation of plantation sites.

(b) Selection of suitable species.

(c) Plantation programme planning.

(d) Working out section-wise plantation schedule and actual plantation operation.

(e) PIC-appointed volunteer squads to protect reforested areas, obviating the expensive and ineffective alternative of fencing.

(iii) *Health Education*

(a) Dissemination of the basic knowledge of the human anatomy, of the body functions and the pathology of common ailments.

(b) Education about public sanitation and personal hygiene.

(c) Antenatal and child care.

(d) Propagation of home remedies.

(e) Dental care based on traditional methods.

(iv) *Nutrition*

(a) Dissemination of information about the nutritional needs of the human body.

(b) Informing the people about nutritional values of the commonly available food material and demonstration of balanced meal from accessible food material.

(c) Ensuring milk consumption up to the optimum level, especially by expectant and nursing mothers and young children.

(v) *Animal Husbandry*

(a) Promoting ecologically sound and economically beneficial livestock policy.

(b) Genetic upgradation of cattle, goat and sheep so as to bring within the scope of feasibility the switch-over from grazing economy to stall-fed economy.

(c) Usage of modern technology, such as embryo transplant to accelerate the pace of genetic upgradation of livestock.

(vi) *Agricultural Extension*

(a) Evolution of a scientific land use pattern.

(b) Identification of rational cropping patterns for the micro-ecosystems.

(c) Experiments in genetic engineering by a carefully selected avant-garde group of local farmers.

(vii) *Conservation*

(a) Educating the farmer about all the aspects of nature conservation.

(b) Promotion of economical use of water.

The core group has studied the aspects of expenditure and income. Its findings can be summarized thus:

Expenditure

Our estimate of expenditure is based on the assumption that over the whole plantation area 10,00,000 trees will survive. There will be a huge surplus of fodder, grasses also. The total cost of the project for a four year span, including recurring and non-recurring items, is estimated to be Re. 1 crore, which works out to Rs. 10 per tree. This figure has to be compared with the official permissible per-tree cost of Rs. 7. The latter does not include the administrative overheads. Moreover, the component of community development is totally absent in the official afforestation efforts. The project as conceived by us, will, besides growing trees, also accomplish another kind of cultivation, that is, human development. The decisive factor in its success will be people's participation, whose worth cannot be measured in monetary terms, because mere expenditure will not concretize participation. For the sake of argument, however, one can safely ascribe at least half of the project as value for participatory community development. When the income from fodder is set-off against residual expenditure the per-tree cost will be further reduced to Rs. 3.

Income

The items of income are firewood, timber, fodder, sisal fibre, gum, honey and tusser silk. Per hectare 1,600 trees will be planted. Survival can be as high as 80 per cent, because gap-filling will be done in the second and third years. Income from fodder can be expected from the third year after plantation. Removal of lower-level twigs and branches from three or four-year-old trees is necessary to train them. This operation will yield marketable fuel of sizable quantities. From the end of the sixth year, the project will be producing surplus income.

Conclusion

The broad spectrum of the project concept can be handled by a voluntary agency having the necessary attributes. In terms of cost-effectiveness, time efficiency and social benefit the out-turn of a voluntary agency will be impressive by far. All things considered, in the voluntary agency option, there is economic prudence and social benefits. If posterity were to be saved from the ultimate curse of desertification our country's greening must take place within a decade by people's power, with only a lacing of money power. For there is an abundance of one and paucity of the other.

6

Problems of Wastelands

Hridai.R.Yadav

1. Introduction

Man has lived in harmany with nature, from immemorial time, in a symbiotic relationship which had ensured that Nature gave of its bounty to people and was, in return, recompensed adequately by the self-regenerating process of eco-development, built into the cultural, socio-economic traditions of human life. Regrettably, in the recent past, man and nature relationship has been shattered, causing incalculable damage to nature and considerable hardship to man. It would be primary task to find out the basic reasons of this collapse, and the remedial measures and effective strategies for reversal of this trend. If we do not succeed, and succeed very late, then the nation will face the prospect of total ecological disaster by the end of this century. For the latest example, *Maldive* Government organised its Cabinet Meeting under the Sea, to draw the attention of international community to restore the ecological imbalances on account of Global Warming.

The problem of wastelands has been appropriately documented. The National Commission on Agriculture stated in its report of 1972 that as much as 175 million hectares out of a total of 266 million hectares which are available for agricultural use are wastelands. The explosive increase of population and increasing desire of the people to exploit marginal and sub-marginal lands for a modicum of returns, unmindful of the further degradation people causes and pressure from industry for raw material needs, defective land use and cropping patterns and inefficient water management have emerged as the main factors. The result is multiple and escalating damage to natural resources, due to both by overexploitation and mismanagement.

There has been alarming challenge for the loss of our forest cover. The forest land area has been 40 million hectares (totalling 74 million hectares in all), is degraded forest land. Our country is loosing 1-5 million hectares of forest land and 12,000 million tonnes of top soil is eroded every year due to deforestation and run-off. The rehabilitation process will be indeed laborious. It takes anything from 500 to 1000 years to restore one inch of top soil and up to 100 years to reestablish a good natural forest. Therefore, it is imperative that this process be taken up on a war footing by mobilizing every conceivable resource and adopting imaginative strategies. Keeping the above facts into consideration, the former Prime Minister of India, Late Sri Rajiv Gandhi established the National Wastelands Development Board in March 1985 with the objective of afforesting five million hectares of land per annum, with emphasis on fuel and fodder plantations.

The relationship of man with environment, the symbiotic bond between the rural poor and forests, especially among tribals has been closest through the years. The traditional rights of such communities to minor forests produce, to grass and fallen drywood for fuel have kept the rural communities going through the centuries. It seems the relationship between man and nature now stands threatened. The legal and otherwise, restrictions, increase, it results in an invitation to the rural poor to cause further degradation, simply because they have no alternative. It is observed that afforestation cannot be achieved by government implementing agencies alone, the main object of afforestation targets have to be perceived as the individual's goals and they should act in union. Therefore, such an endeavour is rendered more difficult because the needs of the community and individuals are at variance with each other. It cannot be reconciled unless poverty amelioration programmes raise the level of living of those below the poverty line. Thus, there has been a slackening of afforestation and absence of support of the local communities for the protection and augmentation of forests.

Various scientific research and development agencies has also been to direct their energies and skills towards result oriented research on improving the ecology and tackling the problem of afforestation in wastelands. Tissue culture for quick multiplication of seedlings, work on location-specific species like *jojoba* on coastal saline wastelands and redeveloping our lost mangrove's system aerial seedlings over areas otherwise inaccessible these are some of many areas in which not only scientists and experts but each individual heed to engage themselves in the integrated sustainable afforestation programme. In this regard, a modern poet Kilmer Joice wrote:

> "I think that I shall never see,
> A poem lovely as a Tree
> Poems are made by fools like me
> But only God can make a tree."

Therefore everyone has to strive to create a true consciousness amongst the entire people.

In view of the above observations, the urgency of the problems of wastelands and its reclamation should be taken as a challenge to meet the increasing demand, of growing cattle and human population, for fodder, fuel wood, fibre, fruits, fisheries and food grains and to restore the ecological and environmental degradation and to improve socio-economic crisis and ensure eco-friendly sustainable development.

2. Wastelands

Wastelands are not a new phenomenon. The term wastelands has been used for common lands usually with less fertile soil, which failed to yield and to give any return to the medieval cultivators. Common man may define the wastelands as land lying uninhabited and uncultivated and which is no longer serving any purpose. The adjective waste has disappeared now because in many cases these common lands are much valued as open spaces. The land which is left out of cultivation, to maintain the fertility status of the soil which is termed as fallow land and often a year if not cultivated, the left out uncultivated land is termed as old fallow land and ofter successive years if the same land is not being brought under cultivations such uncultivated land is termed as banjar land. Stamp[1] appropriately defined wastelands as "Land which has been previously used but which has been abandoned and no further use has been found for it."

A broad definition for wastelands would be "Land which is uncultivated or is presently lying unutilized due to different constraints but had been used previously, which is giving very low actual return, i.e. has low economic potential, is ecologically unstable, or whose top soil has completely lost its fertility status, which has developed toxicity and is, therefore, unfit for the growth of crops and trees due to environmental or anthropogenic problems, has been abandoned and no further use has been found for it."

The land which would not produce the bio-mass as per the soil and water availability, such land may be termed as wastelands.

The land which is lying unuseful due to improper attention and the land is lying vacant or due to excessive grazing, soil erosion, land degradation and due to unfertility and in such land in which agricultural cropping expenditure is higher than the profit accrued out of it, such land is termed as wastelands.

The land which is unuseful due to improper care and management or due to overgrazing, land degradation, and due to non-greenery and due to salinity/alkalinity, the land is non-profitable and cost of agricultural cropping is higher than the productivity, such land is termed as wastelands.

Such land which is ecologically stayable, which is eroded and its productivity capability provides low productivity, are termed as wastelands.

Any such land whose ecological system is not in accordance with the production capability may be called as wastelands.

The land which has lost its production capability due to various reasons including improper care, mismanagement and in which the cost of production is higher than the profit accrued out of it, such type of land may be called as wastelands.

3. Types of Wastelands

The classification of wastelands are being done on the point of view of its utilization, which are useful in different forms of application and cultivation of such lands.

The classification of wastelands in this study has been done on the basis of the land use classification proposed by the Directorate of Economics and Statistics, Ministry of Agriculture. The cultivable wastelands of Amethi has been classified into the following broad categories:

- Waterlogged land
- Usar land
- Banjar land
- Old fallow land
- Follow land
- Other types of wasteland

Fallows other than current fallow land has been further sub-divided into old fallow (2-5 years) land and fallow (1-2 years) land.

Thus in Amethi Block, six types of wastelands have been derived from two important categories of land use, *viz.* cultivable waste and fallow other than the current fallow. Wastelands of all above types exist in Amethi.

In Sultanpur District, two more categories of wastelands are found which are especially :

(i) *Ravine land* : Which is found along both sides of river Gomati. The ravine lands are undulated having sandy soil, in which water retaining capacity is very poor and underground water-table is found in high depth. In the ravine land sarpat, kash, Munj and other natural flora and fauna is found, and

(ii) *Kankar land* : It is found in few patches, in such land due to calcareousness of the soil the hard *kankar pan* does not allow the water percolation. The *kankar pan* is found at one meter depth. The *kankar* land has very low productivity and its reclamation cost is also very high.

The wastelands of Amethi are discussed below :

1. *Water logged Land :* Waterlogged land is that where water-table is at or near the earth's surface and water stands for most of the year and soil pores in the root zones of the crop get saturated with water which inhibits the growth and activity of plants. As a result such lands are left out uncultivated.
2. *Usar Land :* Those fluffy soils which have a whitish or greyish appearance deposited on the surface and are not easily cultivable are commonly known as reh or rehar or usar land.

   The lands which have excessive proportions of soluble salts due to which crop production is seriously hampered are known as salt-affected soils; locally they are known as usar lands.
3. *Banjar Land :* These are the lands which has been taken up for cultivation but are presently out of cultivation for a period of not less than five years. Such lands are left uncultivated for a long period.
4. *Old Fallow Land :* Such lands which were under cultivation but presently are left out of cultivation for a period of not less than two years and not more than five years may be termed as old fallow land.
5. *Fallow Land :* These are the lands which can be taken up for cultivation but temporarily out of cultivation for not less than one year and not more than two years are termed as fallow land.
6. *Other Types of Wastelands :* Other types of wasteland include such lands which cannot as per definition be put under any other above heads. They are mentioned in the village handbook. The other types of wastelands are those which were under cultivation but are presently left out of cultivation for one reason or the other.

Thus, the wastelands have been derived from cultivable wastland and fallows other than current fallow categories of land use.

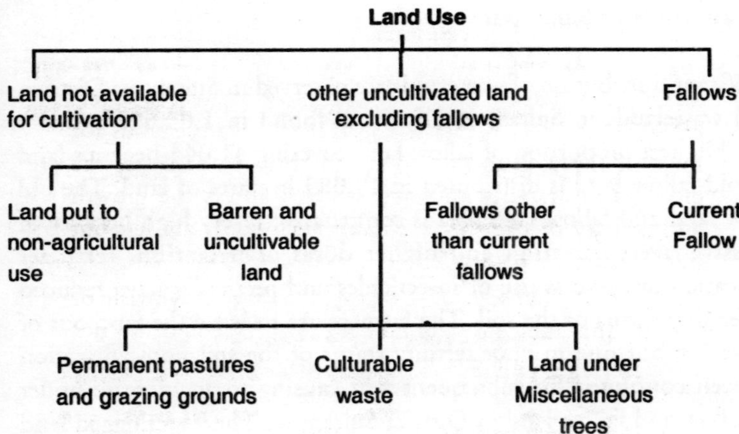

Thus, the above classified cultivable wasteland and fallow other than the current fallow land has been sub-classified as shown in Table 6.1.

Table 6.1
Wasteland

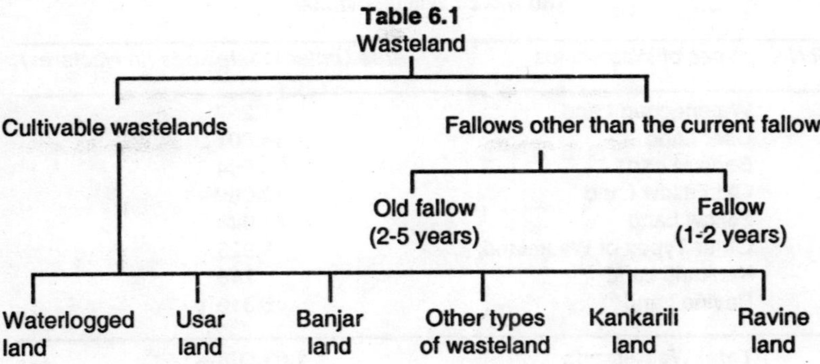

An attempt is being made to describe the wastelands distribution in Sultanpur Dristrict at Block level and special emphasis is being made to analyze the distribution of different types of wastelands at village level, i.e. grass roots level in Amethi Block of District Sultanpur with the view to formulate village action plan at grass roots level to develop extensive action plan for the reclamation of wastelands for the agro-afforestation management to fulfil the increasing demand of growing cattle and human population.

4. Wastelands of Sultanpur

Significant distribution of wastelands are observed in Sultanpur District. Total wastelands in Sultanpur District is found in 1,03,608 hectares land. Highest proportion of fallow land covering 41,044 hectares land and old fallow land is distributed in 19,089 hectares of land. The old fallow land and fallow land area is comparatively very high because of excessive overcultivation and higher doses of irrigation, fertilizer application and excess use of insecticides and pecticides have reduced the fertility status of the soil. The farmers use to leave the land out of cultivation but due to poor fertility status of the soil non-cultivation has been continued for subsequent year causing to an increase under old follow and fallow land in District Sultanpur. The waterlogged land in Sultanpur District is found in 11,297 hectares and area under banjar wasteland is regarded 9,594 hectares. The banjar land are such land which are left our of cultivation for subsequent more than five years.

Table 6.2 : Wasteland 2001

Sl.No.	*Types of Wastelands*	*Area Under Wastelands (in Hactares)*
1.	Waterlogged Land	11,297
2.	Usar Land	14,601
3.	Banjar Land	9,594
4.	Old Fallow Land	19,089
5.	Fallow Land	41,044
6.	Other Types of Wasteland	1,925
7.	Kankarili Land	748
8.	Ravine Land	5,310
	Total Wastelands	**1,03,608**

The area under different types of wastelands are shown in Table 6.2. The area under ravine land is also significant because the undulated ravine lands are found along the both sides of river Gomati. The usar land in Sultanpur District is observed in 14,601 hectares area. While kankarili land in found in 748 hectares area in Sultanpur.

Thus it is evident from Table 6.2 and 6.3 that waterlogged land is found in the low-lying areas and at the tale of canals and due to over-irrigation. The usar land is observed more in those areas where calcareousness; alkalies salinity is found at higher extent and at one meter depth hard *kankarpan* is found which restrict the water percolation due to which the fertility status of the soil used to be reduced and the farmers are bound to leave the land out of cultivation. Similarly, the banjar land, old fallow land and fallow lands are observed in most of the villages because the farmers often use to leave the land out of cultivation to restore and maintain the fertility status of the soil. The kankarili land is found in few areas where calcareousness is found in the soil while ravine land is found along with the both sides of river Gomati where undulated topography and sandy soils are found. The other types of wastelands are found mostly in all villages of Sultanpur. The category-wise distribution of wastelands at Block level in Sultanpur are described in detail.

Waterlogged Land in Sultanpur District

Waterlogged lands are recorded in the low-lying areas where excess natural rainy water or overirrigated water and leftover water from canal gets accumulate in such areas where water-table is very close or low to the earth surface. The excess water on the earth surface does not allow the agricultural productivity and due to very poor agricultural productivity, the farmers use to leave such land out of cultivation. Proportionately very high waterlogged land is observed in Jamo and Gauriganj Block. Very low waterlogged land is seen in Pratappur Kamaicha and Sangrampur Blocks because in Pratappur Kamaicha Block undulated uplands are available and in Sangrampur Block there is no low-lying area and no overexcess irrigation water areas are found. Proportionately-high waterlogged land is recorded in Dhanpatganj, Kurebhas, followed by Jaisinghpur Blocks where the excess irrigation water is accumulated in the low-lying area nearer to the Sharada Canal. The excess water is accumulated in the low-lying areas which has taken into the form of a jhil. This jhil has much soil silting process, due to which overirrigated water has affected more the cultivated land leading towards an increase in the area under waterlogged land. Waterlogging has affected maximum areas and in such areas there is no agricultural productivity and the land is left out of cultivation which is a very serious problem for the farmers because it has not only affected agricultural productivity of the area but it has caused various water-borne diseases and it has damaged not only the income and wealth of the farmers but also the health of the deprived rural multitudes.

Usar Land

The usar lands are such areas where calcareousness and alkalinity/salinity is found and pH value of the soil is found more and water percolability used to be very poor and the soil does not have retaining capacity of the lands. Proportionately very high usar land in hectares are found in the Akhandnagar Block followed by Kadipur, Dostpur, and Dhanpatganj Blocks of District Sultanpur. High usar land area in hectares are observed in Gauriganj, Bhnetua and Dubepur Blocks of District Sultanpur. Very low distribution of usar land in Sultanpur District is seen in Pratappur Kamaicha Block, Shahgarh, Sangrampur Blocks while low usar land area in hectares are recorded in Baldirai, Amethi, Blocks of District Sultanpur. Thus, the problem of usar land is an acute adverse situation in Sultanpur District due to poor fertility status of soil and very low agricultural productivity. Thus, the restoration of usar land or the reclamation of usar land is very important and to improve the ecological imbalance and socio-economic crisis of the area.

Banjar Land

The banjar land is found in the 9,594 hectares land in Sultanpur District. Very high banjar land in hectares are found in Baldirai Block of District Sultanpur, because due to very low fertility status of the soil and to re-maintain the fertility status of the soil land is left-out of cultivation for more than five years. High banjar land area in hectares are seen in Kunwar Block of Sultanpur District, where due to undulated topography in few villages and salinity problem of soil in some villages have caused an increase under the area of the banjar land. Due to very poor fertility status of the soil, farmers are bound to leave such land out of cultivation for more than five years. Very low area in hectares under banjar land is observed in Shahgarh Block, Sangrampur and Protappur Kamaicha Blocks of District Sultanpur. Proportionately low area in hectares under banjar land is found in Musafirkhana, Gauriganj, and Amethi Blocks of the District Sultanpur. The reclamation and restoration of banjar land is very important task to improve the ecological imbalance and socio-economic crisis of the deprived multitudes of the rural poor.

Old Fallow Land

The old fallow land is found in 19,089 hectares area in Sultanpur District. Proportionately very high area in hectares of old fallow land is seen in Kunbhar and Jaisinghpur Blocks of Sultanpur District while high old fallow land area in hectares are observed in Kadipur, Akhand Nagar, Kunwar, Dhanpatganj, and Shukul Bajar Blocks of Sultanpur District. The old fallow land is left out of cultivation for two to five years with the view to restore and remaintain the fertility status of the soil. Very low area in hectares under old fallow land is found in Jagdishpur, Musafirkhana, and Pratappur Kamaicha Blocks of Sultanpur District. It is observed that old fallow land is distributed moderately in Sultanpur District. The old fallow land has been left out of cultivation to maintain the fertility status of the soil but due to negligence and due to low fertility of the soil and poor economic conditions and ignorance of the farmers it had become very difficult to restore the fertility status of the soil from two to three years. The old fallow land can be easily reclaimed for agro-afforestion activities with the view to meet the increasing demand of growing cattle and human population of the District Sultanpur.

Fallow Land

The fallow lands are such lands which has been left out of cultivation from one to two years, with the view to restore and remaintain the fertility status of the soil. Proportionately, the distribution of fallow land is higher than the other categories of wastelands found is Sultanpur District. There are 41,044 hectares fallow land is Sultanpur District. Due to over and excess cropping of land the fertility status of the soil have been reduced, and due to poor agricultural productivity and adoption of traditional agricultural techniques, it had become very difficult to maintain the fertility status of the soil and the cost of agricultural production is higher than the profitability due to which the farmers are bound to leave such land out of cultivation which has caused ecological degradation and socio-economic imbalances of the area. Very high fallow land in hectares are found in Dhanpatganj, and Akhand Nagar Blocks followed by Jagdishpur and Kunbhar Blocks in Sultanpur District. Very low area, in hectares, of fallow land is seen in Sangrampur Block followed by Motigarpur and Amethi Blocks of District Sultanpur. It is observed that the fallow land can be very earily brought under cultivation through appropriate attention including proper doses of fertilizer, high yielding variety of seeds, improved agricultural cropping pattern and requisite irrigation system as per requirement of the soil and crop.

Other Types of Wastelands

The other types of wastelands are found in 1,925 hectares in the district Sultanpur. Very high area from 90-99 hectares under other types of wastelands are found in Jagdishpur, Gauriganj, Amethi, Kunbhar, Jaisinghpur, and Kadipur blocks of District Sultanpur. The other types of wastelands are such areas which are not specifically categorized as wastelands but are lying waste miscellaneously due to various reasons. Very low area under other types of wastelands less than 60 hectares are recorded in Shuḳul Bazar Block of District Sultanpur. It is obsesved that the other types of wastelands distribution in hectares at Block level are very nominal. The other types of wastelands area in hectares varies from 50 hectares to 99 hectares at Block level in district Sultanpur. It has been recorded that the other types of wastelands which are not being utilized miscellaneously can be utilized very easily at least afferestation programmes to restore the ecological and environmental degradation of the area. In the other types of wastelands departmental and community afforestation programme may be implemented with the view to obtain common minimum requirements of the growing population.

Kankarili Land

The kankarili land is found in 748 hectares area which is shown in Table

6.2. The *kankarili* land is found only in 10 Blocks of District Sultanpur while 13 blocks are not having *kankarili* land. The *kankarili* land is not observed in the blocks of Musafirkhana, Gauriganj and Amethi Tehsils, followed by Akhandnagar and Lambhua Blocks of Kadipur and Lambhua Tehsils respetively. Prorortionately more than 100 hectares *kankarili* land is found in Dhanpatganj, Kunbhar and Kunwar Blocks of Sultanpur District, More than 50 hectares to 80 hectares *kankarili* land is observed in Jaisinghpur, and Bhadainya Blocks while Dostpur Block has 45 hectares *kankarili* land followed by Kadipur and Dubepur Blocks having 35 hectares of *kankarili* land and 30 hectares *kankarili* land in Motijaspur Block while very low 10 hectares *kankarili* land is recorded in Pratappur Kamaicha Block of District Sultanpur. Proportionately, the calcariousness is found very high in *kankarili* land and kankar pan is found in the soil which creates hindrance in the germination of species and plants because of poor percolation of water and due to calcareousness the plants does not grow due to which the *kankarili* land is left out of cultivation and such lands are lying wastes without any use which has led to ecological and environmental degradation.

Ravine Land

Ravine land has undulated topography and sandy soils which has very poor water retaining capacity due to which agro-afforestation programmes are not successfully implemented, In the ravine land sarpat, kash, Munj and shrubs are grown naturally and the soil erorion in the ravine land is comparatively higher than the other types of land due to sandyness and undulated topography and poor water retaining capacity of the soil and poor fertility status of the soil the ravine land is left out of cultivation. The ravine land is found along with the both sides of Gomati river. There are no ravine land in Jamo, Shahgarh, Gauriganj, Amethi, Bhnetua, Bhadan, Sangrampur and Akhandnagar Blocks of District Sultanpur. Very high more than 600 hectares ravine land is found in Musafirkhara, Baldirai and Kunwar Block of Sultanpur District. There are 489 hectares ravine land in Dhanpatganj and 428 hectares ravine land in Kurebhan Blocks followed by 359 hectares in Bhadainya Block and Shukul Bazar with 340 hectares and Jagdishpur having 360 hectares ravine land and 208 hectares ravine land in

Jaisinghpur blocks of District Sultanpur. Low ravine land is observed in Dubeper with 185 hectares and Dostpur with 185 hectares and Lambhua having 136 hectares. Kadipur has 110 hectares ravine land while very low 30 hectares of ravine land is found in Pratappur Kamaicha Block of District Sultanpur. It is very difficult to reclaim the ravine land under cultivation due to very high water-table and poor retaining water capacity and undulated topography and sandy soil but ravine land can be easily reclaimed for social-forestry programmes to fulfil the increasing demand of fibre, fuel wood, fodder need of the growing cattle and human population and to restore the ecological crisis of the area and improve the socio-econmic crisis of people.

Total Wastelands

There are 1,03,608 hectares total wastelands in Sultanpur District. The proportionately, very high area under wastelands in hectares are observed in Akhandnagar and Dhanpatganj Block of district Sultanpur followed by Kurebhan Block. Comparatively high area in hectares of wastelands are seen in Jagdishpur, Jamo, Jaisinghpur, Dubepur and Bhadainya Blocks of District Sultanpur while very low area in hectares under total wastelands are observed in Sangrampur, and Kadipur Blocks, while low area in hectares of total wastelands are found in Baldirai, Shahgarh, Amethi, Bhnetua and Pratappur Kamaicha Blocks of the District Sultanpur. The wastelands available in Sultanpur District are lying unutilized due to ignorance and techno-socio-economic backwardness, and such lands can be easily brought under agro-afforestation activities adopting techno-scientific methods of reclamation. No doubt such reclaimed wastelands can be utilized for agro-afforestation programmes to meet the increating demand of fuel wood, fodder, fibre, fruits, fisheries and food grains (F^6) which will be helpful in restoring the ecological and environmental degradation and improving the socio-economic crisis of the deprived multitudes living in the villages of Sultanpur District.

5. Wastelands in Amethi Block

The wastelands in Sultanpur District are significantly distributed. Similarly, wastelands in Amethi Block are also distributed significantly except kankarili and ravine land are not observed in Amethi due to different soil structure and topographical situations. There are 11.36 per cent total wastelands found in Amethi Block of District Sultanpur. Other types of wastelands are 0.35 per cent followed by 0.47 per cent area under waterlogged land and 1.13 per cent banjar land. Proportionately fallow land has very high percentage (3.87%) area under fallow land followed by 2.56 per cent area under old fallow land in Amethi Block. Thus, the wastelands in Amethi Block has signigicant distribution which has become great concern of the planners. If the control and check for the growth of wastelands are not properly planned and implemented, then, it will have very adverse affect on ecological and environmental conditions of Amethi and subsequently socio-economic crisis among the people living in the area. The proportionate distribution of wastelands categories at village level are described in this study.

Table 6.3 : Wastelands in Amethi

S.No.	*Types of Wasteland*	*Area in Percentage*
1.	Waterlogged land	0.47
2.	Usar land	1.89
3.	Banjar land	1.13
4.	Old fallow land	2.56
5.	Fallow land	3.87
6.	Other types of wasteland	0.35
	Total Wastelands	**10.27**

Waterlogged Land

The waterlogged land at village level in Amethi Block is significantly distributed which is less than 1.38 per cent. Proportionately very high percentage of waterlogged land is observed in Nainha Bartali, Dehra, Saraiya Duban, Chaturbhujpur and Ram Daipur villages of Amethi Block which is shown in Table- 6.3. The moderate waterlogged land from 0.80 per cent to 1 per cent is found in Loniapur, Jangal Ram Nagar, Bhaganpur, Mahmadpur, Maharajpur and Gaderi villages of Amethi block. Very low percentage less than 0.10 per cent waterlogged land is observed in Kherauna, Parsanwa and Kushi Tali Villages of

Amethi Block while 0.10 per cent to 0.20 per cent waterloggel land is recorded in Himmatgarh, Agahar, Dhandhudhan, Nunwawa, Tala, Trilokpur, Sarai Khema, Rebha, Mahso, and Hathkilla villages of Amethi Block. Very insignificant distribution of waterlogged land is found in the central, northern and eastern villages of the Amethi Block because these villages are less affected by the excessive accumulation of surface water and most of the villages are having appropriate outlet/drainage system for access accumulated water. The overall proportionate distribution of waterlogged land at village level in Amethi is significantly low. Even this can be checked and waterlogged lands can be reclaimed by constructing proper drainage system as outlets for the accumulated surface natural rain or excess irrigation water and adopting appropriate management of irrigation water and underground water.

Usar Land

The usar lands are those soils which have whitish or greyish appearance on the surface of the land and the usar lands are not easily cultivable due to reh or usar. The usar land has excessive proportions of soluble salts due to which cropping of agriculture is seriously hampered, such lands are termed as salt-affected soils and these soils are locally known as usar land in Amethi area. Proportionately very high, more than 3 per cent usar land area is found in Trilokpur, Saraikhema, Umapur-ganapatti and Bhusahari villages of Amethi Block. Moderate usar land area from 2 per cent to 3 per cent is recorded in Benipur, Dedhpasar, Rebha, Ramdaipur, Lohasta, Chaturbhujpur, Maharajpur, Purabgaon and Gaderi villages of Amethi Block. Very low less than 1 per cent of usar land is observed in Kherauna, Parsanwa, Hathkila, Loniapur, Katara Maharani, Kushi Tali, Naraini, Saraiya Duban and Himmatgarh villages of Amethi Block.

The usar land of Amethi Block can be easily reclaimed for social forestry especially fuel wood and fodder plants which can survive and sustain in such usar land, but a few decades before the usar land of Amethi had a very negative role in the agricultural economy of the rural poor of Amethi, because in such usar land farmers were not able to grow any crop or plant, due to which the usar land had been left out of cultivation from several years. In view of the non-fertility and agricultural productivity of the usar land, it had been the common pro-verb among the peoples of Amethi that, *"Amethi Na hot usar, Enha ke log hot Daiv se Dusar"* which mean that *If Amethi had no usar land then the people of Amethi would have been next after the God.* But at present the usar land of Amethi are being easily reclaimed through latest scientific techniques, and high yielding variety of seeds/plants and new irrigational system etc has made the farmers to reclaim the usar land to meet the increasing demand of growing population and cattle for firewood and fodder respectively. Various Government and Non-Government agencies have been involved for the reclamation of usar land but it could not obtain the goals as per the target because there was lack of people participation and interest and involvement of the rural poor has been ignored. The involvement of the people and their interest in the planning, process of reclamation of usar land agro-afforestation on usar land and its maintenance and management up to distribution of profits accrued out of it may provide a new way to reclaim the usar land to maintain the ecological imbalances and improve the environmental and socio-economic crisis of the people of Amethi.

Banjar Land

The banjar land in Amethi at village level are significantly distributed which is mentioned in Table 6.2. Proportionately very high percentage of banjar land more than 4 per cent is found in Loniapur and Raipurfulwari villages of Amethi Block. High percentage of banjar land varying between 3.50 per cent to 4 per cent is found in Parsanwa, Benipur, Hathkila, Darkha, Chaturbhujpur, Mochwa villages of Amethi Block of Sultanpur District. Very low percentage of banjar land less than 1.50 per cent is recorded in Kherauna, Saraikhema, Katara Maharani, Agahar, Ramgarh and Bhusahari villages of Amethi Block. The banjar land are those lands which are left out of cultivation for a period of not less than five years. Thus, the banjar lands are left uncultivated for a long period which can be easily brought under cultivation to meet the increasing demand of growing people. The C-2 scientific technobogy i.e. the system which are available with the farmers and within the villages can be adopted to reclaim the banjar land i.e. application of compost/waste materials, proper plugging, appropriate application of organic and inorganic fertilizer, insecticides and pesticides, high yielding variety of seeds and plants and proper imitation system etc. may be an asset which can be adopted as measures for the reclamation of wastelands for fuel wood, fodder, fibre, fruits and food grain production to restore the ecological and environmental degradation and improving the socio-economic crisis of the deprived multitudes of the Amethi people.

Old Fallow Land

The old fallow lands are those lands which are left out of cultivation from two to five years time with the view to re-maintain the fertility status of the soil. The old fallow lands are those degraded lands whose fertility status to grow the crops has been reduced due to some reason or the other including excess or overcropping of the land. The farmers could not adopt the crop rotation cycle and are unable to adopt latest scientific and technical methods of cropping, as per the ignorance of the farmers the land has lost the fertility status of the soil due to which such lands has been left-out of cultivation in anticipation of maintaining the fertility status of the soil. Proportionately very high percentage of old fallow land more than 5 per cent is found in Hathkila village. High distribution of old fallow land between 3 per cent to 4 per cent is observed in the Rebha, Loniapur, Ramdaipur, Jangal Ramnagar, Naraini, Ramgarh and Himmatgarh villages of Amethi Block while very low percentage of old fallow land is found in Kherauna, Katara Fulkunwar villages of Amethi Block. Proportionately low percentage of old fallow land varying from 1 per cent to 2 per cent is recorded in Parsanwa, Benipur, Mahso, Raidaipur, Saraikhema, Trilokpur, Tala, Kushitali, Bhaganpur, Loharta, Darkha, Korarigirdharshah, Nuanwa, Umapurganapatti, Kuhra, Kakwa, Saidpur, Saraiya Duban, Mahmadpur, Agahar, Purabgaon, Bhusahari and Gangauli villages of the Amethi Block. It is observed that the old fallow land is significantly distributed at village level in Amethi Block of Sultanpur District.

Fallow Land

Fallow land at village level in Amethi are very significantly distributed in Amethi. Very high percentage of fallow land more than 6 per cent is found in Hathkila, Saraikhema villages of Amethi block. Proportionctely high percentage varying between 3 per cent to 4 per cent is recorded in Katara Fulkunwar, Dedhpasar, Mahso, Loniapur, Katara Maharani, Darkha, Korarigirdharshah, Dhandhudhar, Kuhra, Saraiya Buban, Agahar and Naraini Bartali villages while 4.15 per cent fallow land is observed in Chaturbhujpur village of Amethi Block. Moderate distribution of fallow land from 2 per cent to 3 per cent is observed in Kherauna, Benipur, Rebha, Raidaipur, Raipurfulwari, Jangal Ramnagar, Kushitali, Nuanwa, Naraini, Saidpur, Maharajpur, Purabgaon, Dehra, Bhusahari and Gangauli villages of Amethi Block. Very low percentage of fallow land less than 1.5 per cent is recorded in Mochawa, Kakawa, Mahmadpur, Parsanwa, Ramdaipur, Trilokpur and Loharta villages of Amethi Block of the Sultanpur District. The fallow land can be easily reclaimed for agro-afforestation activities because the fallow land has been left out of cultivation due to poor fertility status of the soil and poor agricultural productivity, in which agricultural cropping expenditure used to be higher than the benefit accrued out of cropping on the fallow land. The fallow land has been left out of cultivation by the farmers to maintain the fertility status of the soil. The fallow land can be easily brought under cultivation through adopting latest agricultural scientific techniques reclaiming fallow land thus agro-afforestation management on fallow land should be adopted to meet the increasing demand of growing cattle and human population for fuel wood, fodder, fibre, fruits, and food grain. The awareness of the farmers for adopting proper agricultural cropping pattern, proper attention to maintain the fertility status of the soil, the adoption of appropriate agricultural scientific technology for reclamation of fallow land, proper doses of organic and inorganic amendments, use of insecticides and pesticides, high yielding variety of seeds, proper doses of irrigation and other copping techniques will be an asset for the restoration of fallow land and to maintain the ecological imbalances of the area.

Other Types of Wastelands

The other types of wastelands are those lands which are lying unutilized miscellaneously but it can be brought under use for some purpose or the other including social-forestry programmes to meet the increasing need of the growing population. Proportionately very high percentage of other types of wastelands more than 5 per cent is found in Kherauna, Parsanwa, Benipur, Katara Fulkunwar and Dedhpasar villages of Amethi Block, while high percentage of other types of wastelands between 4 per cent to 5 per cent is observed in Mahso, Loniapur, Jangal Ram Nagar, Korarigirdhar Shah, Umapurganapatti, Mochwa, and Nainaha Bartali villages of Amethi Block. Very low percentage between 1 per cent to 2 per cent other types of wastelands are found is Saraikhema, Trilokpur, Tala, Loharta, Saraiya Duban and Himmatgarh villages of Amethi Block of Sultanpur District. The other types of wastelands are not under use for various miscellaneous reasons which can be easily brought under social-forestry programmes for maintenance of ecological and environmental imbalances of the area. The reclamation of other types of wastelands will be helpful in restoring the ecological and environmental crisis and also improving the socio-economic crisis of the area. The other types of wastelands can be reclaimed for social-forestry programmes to obtain especially fuel wood and fodder needs of the growing human and cattle population respectively.

Wastelands in Amethi Block

The wastelands in Amethi Block at village level are significantly distributed. Very high percentage of wastelands more than 14 per cent has been recorded in Hathkila, Dedhpasar, Loniapur villages of Amethi Block while high percentage of wastelands between 12 per cent to 14 per cent are observed in Benipur, Katara Fulkunwar, Rebha, Saraikhema, Dhandhudhar, Maharajpur and Nainha Bartali villages of Amethi Block. Very low percentage of wastelands less than 8 per cent has been found in Kushitali, Loharata, Korarigirdharshah, Nuanwa, Kakwa, Saidpur, Purabgaon, Ramgarh, Himmatgarh and Gaderi villages of the Amethi block. While low percentage of wastelands varying between 8 per cent to 12 per cent are seen in the Gangauli, Bhusahari, Agahar, Mahmadpur, Saraiya Duban, Mochwa, Naini, Kohra, Tala, Bhaganpur, Trilokpur, Mahmadpur, Raidaipur, Mahso and Kherauna villages of the Amethi Block of the District Sultanpur. The wastelands of Amethi Block can be reclaimed through adopting scientific techniques and latest techniques of agro-afforestation system to meet the fuel wood, fodder, fibre, fruits, fisheries and food grain (F^6) requirements of the increasing cattle and human population and maintaining the ecological and environmental degradation crisis of the area.

6. Conclusion

Symbiotic relationship between man and nature is continued from immemorial time. In the past man and nature relationship has been shattered causing incalculable damage to nature which has caused hardship to man. The remedial measures and effective strategies for reversal of this trend has to be searched. The problem of wastelands has been appropriately documented. There has been alarming challenge for loot of our agricultural land which is 175 million hectares and 40 million hectares of forest land which is degraded forest land. Thus, our country is loosing 1.5 million hectares of forest land and about 12,000 million tonnes of top soil is eroded every year. The rural poor depends on the forest resources.

Thus, the problem of wastelands and its reclamation should be taken a challenge to meet the increasing demand of growing cattle and human population in the form of fuel wood, fodder, fibre, fruits, fisheries and food grains etc. with the view to restore ecological and environmental degradation and to improve socio-economic crisis of the area.

The wastelands are those lands which are uncultivable or presently lying unutilized due to different constraints but it had been used previously, which is giving very low actual return, i.e. it has low economic potential and it is ecologically unstable or whose top soil has completely lost its fertility status, which has developed toxicity and is therefore unfit for the growth of crops and tree due to environmental or anthropogenic problems, has been advanced and no further use has been found for it.

The classification of wastelands have been derived from land use categories taking cultivable waste and fallow land. The cultivable wasteland have been sub-divided into waterlogged, usar, banjar, kankarili raivne and other types of wastelands while fallow land other than the current fallow has been sub-divided into old fallow land and fallow land excluding current fallow land. These eight categories of wastelands are available in Sultanpur District. While only six categories of wastelands viz. waterlogged, usar land, banjar land, old fallow land, fallow land and other types of wastelands are found in Amethi Block of Sultanpur District.

Wastelands are significantly distributed in Sultanpur District. There are 1,03,608 hectares of wastelands in Sultanpur District. The fallow lands are found comparatively very high, covering 41,044 hectares land followed by old fallow land having 19,089 hectares land and usar land 14,601 hectares land. The waterlogged land is found in 11,291 hectares area and banjar land in 9,594 hectares area. Similarly, significant area under ravine land along with the Gomati river is found which is spread in 5,310 hectares area and the miscellaneous other types of wastelands are found in 1,925 hectares land while very low area covering 748 hectares kankarili land is observed in Sultanpur District.

Proportionately, the wastelands are very significantly distributed in Amethi Block at village level. There are 11.36 per cent total wastelands found in Amethi Block. Comparatively fallow land area is very high which is 3.87 per cent to the total area of the Block. The old fallow land is found in 2.56 per cent area while usar land is observed in 1.89 per cent area. The other types of wastelands in Amethi Block are recorded 0.35 per cent and waterlogged land covering 0.47 per cent area in Amethi Block of District Sultanpur.

At village level waterlogged land is found very high in Chaturbhujpur, Dehra and Ramdaipur villages while very low waterlogged land is observed in Kherauna, Parsanwa, Kushi Tali villages of Amethi Block.

The usar lands are comparatively very high more than 3 per cent in Bhusahari and Umapurganapatti, Trilokpur, and Saraikhema villages while very low percentage less than 1 per cent usar land is observed in Kherauna, Parsanwa, Hathkila, Loniapur, Katara Maharani, Kushitali, Naraini, Saraiya Duban and Himmatgarh villages of Amethi Block of District Sultanpur.

Banjar lands are significantly distributed in Amethi at village level. Very high percentage of banjar land more than 4 per cent is found in Loniapur, Raipurfulwari villages while very low percentage of banjar land less than 2 per cent is observed in Gaderi, Bhusahari, Ramgarh, Himmatgarh, Agahar, Maharajpur, Saraiya Duban, Loharta, Katara Maharani, Saraikhema, and Kherauna villages of Amethi Block.

Proportionately more than 5 per cent old fallow land is seen in

Hathkilla village and very low percentage old fallow land less than 1 per cent is observed in Kherauna, Katarafulkunwar villages of Amethi Block.

Comparatively very high percentage more than 5 per cent fallow land is seen in Hathkilla, Saraikhema villages of Amethi Block while very low percentage less than 1.5 per cent fallow land is observed in Parsanwa, Benipur, Ramdaipur, Trilokpur, Loharta, Mochwa, Kakwa, Mahmadpur villages of Amethi Block of Sultanpur district.

Other types of wastelands are found very high more than 5 per cent in Kherauma, Parsanwa, Benipur, Katara Fulkunwar villages while very low less than 2 per cent other types of wastelands are seen in Saraikhema, Trilokpur, Tala, Loharta, Saraiya Duban and Himmatgarh villages of Amethi Block.

The total wastelands are very significantly distributed in Amethi Block. Very high percentage of wastelands more than 15 per cent is seen in Dedhpasar village followed by Hathkila (14.32%), Loniapur (14.75%) villages while very low percentage of wastelands less than 8 per cent are recorded in Kushi Tali, Loharta, Korarigirdharshah, Nuanwa, Kakwa, Saidpur, Purabgaon, Ramgarh, Himatgarh and Gaderi villages of Amethi Block of Sultanpur District.

Thus it is observed that the wastelands are significantly distributed at village level not only in Amethi Block but Sultanpur Distrit as a whole, which has become a challenging problem to the planners and developmental agencies engaged at Sultanpur.

It has been recorded during the field survey and action field work programme that the wastelands of Sultanpur and Amethi Block has been left out of cultivation for very smaller reasons and ignorance of the cultivators. Such wastelands can be easily reclaimed adopting latest scientific and technical methods and aplying C-2 scientific technology, i.e. the scientific system available within the village or household itself. The adoption of scientific cropping system/pattern, proper ploughing techniques, appropriate doses of organic and inorganic amendments in the form of fertilizer and application of insecticides and pesticides, appropriate high yielding variety of seeds and plants, proper management system including irrigation and post-harvest technology will be helpful in bringing out the wastelands under proper use to grow fuel wood, fodder, fibre, fruits, fisheries, and food grains to meet the increasing demand of growing cattle and human population on the one hand and restoring the ecological and environmental degradation and imbalances of the area and improving socio-economic crisis of the people of Amethi in Sultanpur District of Uttar Pradesh.

NOTE

1. Stamp L.D., "Land of Britain, Its Use and Misuse", Vol. XV, No. V, 1968, AMU, G.S., Aligarh.

7

Typology and the Mapping Procedures of Wastelands in the Indian Arid Zone

Amal Kumar Sen

Wasteland as a Mapping Unit

Wasteland from the grammarian's point of view is *idle land*. But in actual practice such land is rare. The land which is considered as waste from the agrarian point of view may be a gravelly area or grassland area or saline area which is often used as a mining or grazing or salt extraction (mining) areas and so, from the geographical or cartographic point of view, may not be considered as true wasteland. Similarly, fallow lands including fallow lands other than current fallows (long fallow) and current fallows (short fallow), as classified by the Land Records and Statistics Directorate, may remain idle land in a particular year but from the land use point of view these are agricultural lands. To put them under wasteland may mislead or confuse the planners. The lands which, because of some very limited environmental conditions, cannot be properly utilized and have left idle can be called wastelands. These commonly include the lands classified by the Directorate of Economics and Statistics as *barren* and *unculturable* lands and *culturable wastelands*. The first one refer to those covered by mountains, rocky, sandy and saline lands which cannot be brought under cultivation except at a high cost. Culturable waste includes all lands available for cultivation whether or not taken up for cultivation during the current year or during the last five years or more in the succession. They may be fallow or grassland and covered with shrubs and trees and not put to any use. Strictly speaking, these are marginal lands and partly belong to long fallow. But all these lands—whatever types of wastelands these may be—are often used as grazing ground as well. Scientifically speaking, the barren and unculturable lands only constitute wastelands. But for the planning purposes, it is also desirable to consider the culturable wastes as well in this category so that their resource potentials are also taken into consideration to suggest future land use planning. Considering their behaviour or utilization conditions, it is quite appropriate to include the culturable waste also — where not cultivated — under the category of wastelands. In other words, all areas, which are degraded, depleted, eroded and are often lying idle and cannot be put into proper landuse practices can be referred to as wasteland.

The Basic Resources Studies Division of the Central Arid Zone Research Institute, Jodhpur, has been conducting integrated basic resources survey in the Indian arid zone which includes land utilization survey as one of its components. Through this land utilization survey, the wastelands of the Rajasthan desert have been classified and their extents have been mapped on various scales.

The methodology of survey and mapping and their classifications and extent in the various districts of the arid zone of Rajasthan are described here.

Methodology

The types and extent of wastelands can be best cartographed through land utilization survey by means of field studies and remote sensing techniques, based on the interpretation of the survey of topographical sheets, aerial photographs and landsat imageries, collection of secondary data and available information and subsequent field survey and field checking. Three types of land use maps can be prepared from the resulting details (Sen, 1972, 1977a, 1978; Sen and Shankarnarayan 1978, Shankarnarayan, Sen and Balak Ram, 1982), *viz.* reconnaissance, detailed reconnaissance or semi-detailed and detailed land use maps. These are large-scale maps, in the scales 1:250,000, 1:100,000 to

1:50,000 and 1:50,000 or more in general in the case of reconnaissance, semi-detailed and detailed maps respectively. These maps show the extent and the degree of land use classes and thus depict the actual pattern. These are helpful to delineate or find out the different types of wastelands and to pinpoint the problem areas (Sen, 1977b).

Aerial photo interpretation techniques for wasteland use mapping

Three sets of investigations are carried out prior to a field survey, *viz.* studies on regional aspects, pattern elements and photo developments. These studies have made possible the preparation of photo maps with similar images and interpretation "keys" for field checks (Sen, 1971). Once the photographic images are correlated with the type of land use during the field check, the sequence of events which form a particular land use unit can often be delineated and many aspects of land use, *viz.* cropping pattern, type of wasteland, type of settlement, etc, can be inferred. After field check, the previous interpretation is corrected, where necessary, and final cartographic operations (Sen, 1967) are undertaken (transferring of details, compilation and editing of data, etc.).

Results and Discussion

Wastelands of Western Rajasthān

Based on present land use and integrated basic resources survey in western Rajasthan, the wastelands in western Rajasthan have been mainly classified into four classes: stony, gravelly, saline and sandy. But considering their complexities and restriction of uses, these have been further classified in the course of survey and remote sensing operations as shown in Table 11.1. In western Rajasthan 7,450,176 ha or 33.25 per cent of the land mass comprises wastelands of various categories.

Wastelands have clearly discernible surface features and as such they appear clearly in the photographs (Montape, 1972; Sen, 1972).

The study of pattern aspects and photo elements enables one to distinguish hills, sloping hill sides, gravelly lands, sand dunes and depressional areas in the photographs. These comprise the wastelands in the Indian desert (Sen, 1972). Uncultivated sandy plains and saline lands can also be identified and mapped by photo-interpretation. In the Indian arid zone we have distinguished four types of wastelands—rocky, gravelly, sandy and saline. The photographic characteristics of these wastelands are as follows:

Sandy Waste

The specific photo pattern is a large area covering in a continuous manner and often interrupted by hummocks (sand dunes) of varying sizes. The images are marked by contrasted tones. Sandy hills or dunes are identified by complex or unusual forms. Close examination of stereoscopic pairs are necessary. Dunes are often marked by stippled structure and coarse texture; their sizes and shapes are irregular. Sandy wastelands are often indicated by a diffused boundary. Aerial photographs of the desert region do not show the vegetative cover on the dunes. Dunes are sometimes mantled by grasses which have darker tones than barren sand. A dune on a sandy plain may appear white against a dark background.

Table 7.1 : Wastelands of western Rajasthan

Wasteland category	*Area in ha*	*Per cent of total area of western Rajasthan*
Sandy waste	34,32,120	48.68
Saline waste	1,97,173	2.80
Stony waste	1,49,491	2.22
Gravelly waste	2,89,353	4.10
Rocky waste	21,141	3.14
Rocky and stony waste	1,14,113	1.62
Stony and gravelly waste	60,525	0.85
Rocky and gravelly waste	6,64,411	9.42
Sandy waste with open scrubs	9,96,762	14.14
Rocky and gravelly waste with open scrubs	9,25,397	13.13
Total	**70,50,176**	

Rocky Wastes

Image structure is mottled, texture is medium to coarse. The specific photo pattern is large area covering in a continuous manner, interrupted by hills and rock outcrops. Scattered trees and shrubs are identified. The images present contrasted colours and tones.

Gravelly Waste

The specific photo pattern is large or small area in a continuous manner. Tone variation is medium to light. The presence of the gravels is marked by a close arrangement of dots, giving a coarse texture to the photo image.

Saline Waste

It is easier to identify and locate saline wastes on the photographs due to the greyish white or ash-coloured tone of the image as a result of salt formation on the surface of the land. In the arid zone, the "playas" or saline depressions often form saline wastelands. These can be easily identified in the photographs.

A survey of wastelands without the help of aerial photographs will be a very costly and time-consuming task.

Landsat Imageries and Wasteland Survey

The feasibility of using Landsat imagery for mapping earth resources and monitoring of desertification was studied by (1) interpreting the natural resources of Rajasthan and of the surrounding regions on a false colour composite mosaic of Landsat imagery, (2) by semi-detailed mapping of the natural resources, monitoring of desertification and temporal changes from one scene covering the Middle Luni Basin by both visual interpretation and digital analysis (Shankarnarayan and Singh, 1979), and (3) Land utilization survey and mapping in the districts of Jaisalmer, Churu and Sri Ganganagar by using and interpreting bands 4, 5, 6, 7 of Landsat imageries—false true colours by an Adcol Viewer.

On the basis of survey it has been possible to classify and delineate the area of wastelands of various categories of the western Rajasthan.

The land use data on the districts of Jhunjhunu, Barmer, Jalore (Part) (Pali), (Part) and Sikar are based on compilation and projection of revenue data and interpretation of Survey of India toposheets, aerial photographs and Landsat imageries (Mruthyunjaya, Malhotra and Sen, 1983; Sen, 1978). The revenue data are based on four year averages (1977-78 to 1980-81). The data relating to other districts are based on field survey on the basis of aerial Photo-Landsat interpretations and field investigations on sample basis to find out the relationship between the findings of the laboratory interpretations or analysis, and their corresponding ground features. Table 7.2 indicates that a fairly satisfactory delineation of the various types of wastelands in the arid zone of Rajasthan has been achieved. Table 7.2 also indicates that the district-wise area under different categories of wastelands and enumerated from the land use maps prepared by the institute on various scales (1:250,000, 1:100,000 and 1:50,000).

Definitions and descriptions of the wastelands classified are shown in Appendix-I.

Acknowledgements

Grateful thanks are due to Dr. K.A. Shankarnarayan, Director, and to Dr. R.P. Dhir, Head, Basic Resources Studies Division, CAZRI, for their keen interest in the work. Thanks are also due to the staff of cartography section, CAZRI for their help in various ways.

Table 11.2 : Distribution of wastelands in arid districts of western Rajasthan (India) (based on remote sensing and field surveys).

District	*Sandy waste*	*Saline waste*	*Stony waste*	*Gravelly waste*	*Rocky waste*	*Rocky & Stony waste*	*Stony & gravelly waste*	*Rocky & gravelly waste*	*Sandy waste with open scrubs*	*Rocky & gravelly with open scrubs*	*Total & % to total area of the Dist.*
Jaisalmer	900315	95097	–	–	–	58909	–	604611	991960	924031	3634423
%	(24.77)	(2.62)				(1.62)		(18.28)	(27.29)	(25.42)	(87.88)
Barmer	362302	14326	7629	78733	4315	12593	21112	–	722	101	501974
%	(72.17)	(2.85)	(1.52)	(15.34)	(0.86)	(2.51)	(4.23)		(0.14)	(0.14)	(17.82)
Bikaner	1368550	16570	–	–	31900	–	–	–	–	–	1417020
%	(96.58)	(1.17)			(2.25)						(49.12)
Jodhpur	412830	24470	121300	122390	–	–	–	–	–	–	682790
%	(60.46)	(3.58)	(18.03)	(17.93)							(30.79)
Churu	44844	6591	–	–	–	2084	803	–	2726	–	57100
%	(78.54)	(11.54)				(3.65)	(1.09)	–	(4.78)	–	(3.39)
Sri Ganganagar	287378	14073)	–	–	–	–	–	–	–	–	301451
%	(95.33)	(4.67)									(14.77)
Jhunjhunu	7292	–	–	6330	14231	–	–	–	71	–	24924
%	(29.25)			(25.40)	(45.06)				(8.29)		(4.20)
Sikar	10499	2000	5205	26453	6083	19627	–	–	1101	73	71041
%	(14.79)	(2.83)	(2.95)	(37.23)	(8.56)	(27.62)			(1.54)	(0.10)	(9.17)
Jaipur	8700	16500	–	–	–	20900	38500	–	–	–	84600
%	(10.28)	(19.5)				(24.70)	(45.52)				(4.18)
Pali	18473	7546	5250	46025	10036	–	–	–	130	306	178144
%	(10.37)	(2.24)	(2.95)	(25.83)	(56.34)				(0.10)	(0.17)	(14.49)
Jalore	10937	–	8297	9491	63248	–	–	–	–	806	96709
%	(11.30)		(9.57)	(9.57)	(69.55)					(0.83)	(9.15)
Total	3432120	197173	149481	289353	221141	114113	60525	664411	996762	925397	7050176
%	(48.68)	(2.80)	(2.12)	(4.10)	(3.14)	(1.62)	(0.85)	(9.42)	(14.14)	(13.13)	(100.00)

Note: Area in hectare and per cent to total Dist. Wasteland, shown in bracket

APPENDIX-I

DEFINITION OF THE CLASSIFICATION OF WASTELANDS IN WESTERN RAJASTHAN

S.No.	*Classification*	*Definition of the classification*
1.	Sandy waste	These cover barren sand dunes—both stabilized and shifting and sandy plains (barren) which cannot be brought under cultivation unless at a high cost but can be put under grassland and subsequently as a rangeland. These are depleted and degraded lands with high biotic interference where fresh depositions of sand are still going on plantation in the form of shelter belt and windbreak are recommended.
2.	Saline waste	These include saline flats, salt infested areas and saline depressions and ranns (depressions) which are not suitable for cultivation but are often used as grazing ground or for extration of salts. In the marginal lands of the saline infested areas, sometimes, like that of the 'Mendah' basin where it joins the Shambar lake salt tolerant crops are grow—these lands however, should be put under saline waste. These are depleted lands and unfit for cultivation. These low-lying areas or depressions (rann) serve as the basin of inland drainage.
3.	Stony waste	These areas are concentrated along the sloping hill sides and piedmont areas where disintegrated rocks due to weathering is the dominating surface feature. Due to agglomeration of stones, cultivation is not possible but grazing may be conducted in the intermittent areas covered with grass and isolated trees. Effective soil depth is poor and a limiting factor for agricultural use. Forestry should be the proper landuse unless mining for building stones or others is economically beneficial. These are degraded and highly eroded lands. These are also very poor range lands.
4.	Rocky waste	This includes the bare hills and sloping hillsides where the rocks are exposed due to prolonged erosion and weathering. The hills are highly denuded and cannot be put under economic use except quarrying where the rocks are suitable to be used as building materials. Forestry can be recommended.

5.	Gravelly waste	These occur in piedmont areas, foothills and plains which are covered by rock fragments caused due to weathering or by drifted pebbles or glacia during the geological pest. Such areas are locally known as Magra land. These are not suitable for agriculture and the same is hardly practised unless a depressed area. Silvipastoral is the only land use system that can be suggested.
6.	Rocky and stony waste	Often the hills are rocky wastes and the adjacent sloping hillsides and foothills cover very small area to be mapped in medium scale (up to 1:50,000). Here the two are grouped together and put under one mapping unit. This is necessary because their development should be considered together. These are highly degraded and eroded land and can hardly be put under cultivation. Forestry and silvipastoral are the alternate land use. Such unit covers small isolated areas.
7.	Rocky and gravelly waste	These are quite large areas where Magra lands or gravelly wastelands are associated with isolated hills either monadnocks or inselberge on peneplane or pediplane surface. Soil being shallow not suitable for cultivation but can be recommended for Silvipastoral and forestry. These are highly eroded and degraded lands.
8.	Stony and gravelly waste	These are undulating plains of large areas on piedmont where gravels and stones are equally predominant. These are degraded and eroded often covered with grasses and used as grazing land. Silvipasture is the recommended land use.
9.	Sandy waste with open scrub lands	These cover vast areas of idle sandy plains, sandy undulating plain and interdune plains with barchanoid dunes and sandy hummocks. Due to little biotic interference, these sandy wastelands are covered with scattered shrubs and wild grasses. These occur extensively on western and northern parts of Jaisalmer district, western Barmer, western Churu and western Bikaner. Fresh sand deposition is common. In many cases, the grasses do not survive for more than a few months after the rain. The shrubs mostly include *Aerva tomentasa* (Bin), *Calligonum polygonoides* (Phog), *Euphoriba tirucallia* (Phohar), *Panicum turqidum, Eleusine compressa,* etc. Prominent grass covers are *Lasiurus sindicus, Fleusine compressa, Cenchrus biflorus, Cymopogon jwarancusa, C. prejpru, Cyperus jaevigatus, Citrullus colonthis, Molligo mudicanllis, Boerharia diffusa* etc.

10. Rocky and gravelly waste with open scrub land. — *Silvipastute in the recommended landuse*: These are the types of lands as described in No. 7 and associated with desert or scattered grasses and scrub lands like that of the previous one described. These are actually the foothills and gravelly piedmonts with isolated hills in Jaisalmer, Churu, Bikaner and Barmer where it often exists in the form of vast stretches of lands and in isolated patches along the Aravalli foothills in Sikar, Pali and Jhunjhunu districts ground flora are often consist of *Eleusine compressa, Dactyloctenium sandicu, Aristida, funiculata, Cymbopogon jawarancusa* and *Lasiurus sindicus*. Silvipasture is the alternate land use.

REFERENCES

Chowdhry, Kamla (1985). On wastelands, *The Ind. Magazine* 5(10), 66 67.

Montapa, F. (1972). Aerial photographs and their use for locating and mapping wastelands of India. *Bulletin No. 44, Ind. Nat. Sci. Acad.*, pp. 59-66.

Mruthyunjaya, Malhotra, S.P. and Sen, A.K. (1983). Technological possibilities of agricultural growth and stability in western Rajasthan — An Assessment, *Ann. Arid Zone* 22(1), 121-133.

Sen, A.K. (1967). Documentation and cartography of the Base map for coordinated land survey—Based on aerial photographs. *Ann. Arid Zone* 6(2), 170-177.

——. (1972). Land utilization mapping to estimate the wastelands of arid zone in Rajasthan by photo interpretation techniques. *Bulletin No. 44, Ind. Nat. Sci. Acad.*, pp. 67-71.

——.(1977a). Land use mapping by aerial photo interpretation technique. Desert ecosystem and its improvement. *CAZRI Monograph No. 1* (Ed. H.S. Mann), pp. 85-100.

——.(1977b). Aerial photo interpretation to analyse land use pattern of sand dunes. *Geog. Rev. Indi.* 39(4), 346-352.

——.(1978). *Land Use Classification System in Indian Arid Zone. CAZRI Monograph.* No. 9.

——.(1981). Land use pattern and overexploitation. *Dev. Policy and Administration* Rev. H.C.M. Institute, Jaipur 7(1), 75-92.

Sen, A.K. and K.A. Shankarnarayan (1978). Methodology and choice of aerial photographs for composite mapping of integrated land survey in Indian arid zone. *Proc. Aerial Photo Aprec. Seminar S.O.I./Instt. Survey*, pp. 160-163.

Shankarnarayan, K.A., Sen, A.K. and Balak Ram (1982). Analysis of wastelands in arid zone by remote sensing techniques. *Proq. Symp. Res. Surv. for Land use plan. & Bnv. Conserve,* Ind. Soc. Photo interp./N.R.S.A., pp. 54-61.

Shankarnarayan, K.A. and S. Singh (1979). Application of Landsat data for natural resource inventory and monitoring of desertification—Report. Visiting Int. Scientific Programme. Remote Sensing Instt., SPSU, U.S.A.

8

Problems of Wasteland in the District of Munger

R.B. Mandal

Westeland has recently attracted the attention of both government and public, because the land which is not suitable for agriculture can be utilized in a judicious manner for environmental protection and giving sustenance to the ever-increasing population by the process of afforestation, land reclamation and adopting measures for soil conservation services. Although the present administration is using these devices for environmental modification and checking the spread of aridity and environmental degradation, the progress has an almost negative impact due to indifferent attitude of the government machinery to accomplish the task.

This study intends to identify the intensity of wasteland in the district of Munger. It will also analyse the determinants responsible for such a distributions besides suggesting remedial measures for the reclamation and better utilization of wastelands. The measures are necessary for protecting the environment from degradation, desertification and giving sustenance to the ever-increasing population. They are quite essential, in order to reduce the pressure of population on our limited amount of cultivated land. The problem of wastelands and its distribution has been analysed through the various cartographic techniques.

Hypotheses

1. That the distribution of wasteland is governed by the distribution of forests.

2. That the distribution of wasteland is found minimum in areas of relatively high percentage of net sown area.
3. That the areas prone to the hazards of flood and drought possess relatively high amounts of wastelands.

Review of Past Literature

The Indian Council of Agricultural Research[1], Bombay (1957), pointed out that in India there are large tracts of wastelands which are at present under active erosion due to misuse. This can be seen from the naked roots of trees and shrubs often found on wastelands. Some of these lands should be afforested to supply fuel, fodder and the rest put under improved pastures. During the Plan period soil conservation measures in wastelands are to be taken over an area of about 40,486 hectares.

S.N. Singh (1969)[2] analysed the changing pattern of cultivable waste in Kerakat tehsil of Jaunpur district, U.P., in spatio-temporal dimensions. The wastelands have been categorized into four classes: old fallows, current fallows, gardens and other wastes including scrub, barren land, etc. Its regional distribution is quite uneven, the intensity being high in ravine lands and the north-eastern tract. Although the extent of old fallows has recorded a major decline, it has been contended that further reclamation of some of the land is possible.

A.B. Mukherji (1971)[3] has identified the spatial changes in agricultural wastelands in U.P. for the period 1951-1967. Due to various physical and cultural factors, some of the districts have experienced some decrease or increase, whereas the Terai and the Southern hill districts appear to be areas of negative change.

Jasbir Singh (1971)[4] studied the distributional patterns and associated factors of cultivable wasteland in India. He realized that many thinly populated areas have greater potentialities as a source and exporter of foodgrains if their cultivable wasteland potential could be realized through irrigation and improved farming methods.

A. L. Singh (1977)[5] suggested a micro-level survey of cultivable land so that uncultivated land may be brought under cultivation in order to alleviate the food problem in India. The author has tried to estimate the cost of reclamation according to the conditions prevailing in different areas.

S. Pandey (1977)[6] studied the changing pattern of cultivable waste in Pharenda tehsil in U.P., 1941 to 1971. He has also suggested measures for its reclamation. An objective approach is adopted with the help of statistical analysis to show the perceptible changes and spatial distribution of the cultivable wasteland at village level in the whole Tehsil. It has also been suggested that suitable flood control measures should be adopted to reclaim cultivable wasteland.

Explanation of the Problem and the Model

The six types of land come under this type of wasteland, i.e. fallow land, margins of waterbodies, dry areas in the drought prone zone, barren land, bad land topography and the margins of forest.

The factors which are responsible for the development of wasteland are problems of wild beasts and insects, artificial barrier created by the environmental pollution, floods and drought, poor peasants with less technological know-how, infertile land, low-lying or forest covered marginal land, and the areas of low population density.

Measures to be taken for the recovery of land with the waste menace include taming the river water for useful purposes under multi- purpose projects; preparation of flood protective embankments, reclamation of forest covered, waterlogged and sandy diaras for cultivation purposes, afforestation and checking the soil erosion on slopy ground, agricultural land; breachs in river embankment points should be properly plugged, and soil erosion on slopy ground, agricultural land checked besides destocking on cultivated lands which are especially upland plains.

The organizations concerned for the reclamation of wastelands are private agencies, crop authorities, fertilizer corporations, government machinery and the public in general.

In the southern and northern parts of the district of Munger, some of the abovementioned factors are responsible for further intensification of the problem due to poor reclamation measures. Year after year, the recurrence of the problem of floods even after some sort of reclamation measures favour the increased expanse of wasteland which may be known as the force of cumulative causation as a closed system.

Sectoral Model for the Decline of Wasteland

Due to increasing population, say, since A.D. 1800, more and more wasteland has been brought under cultivation and hence both the help of cultivators and recent measures adopted by the Government have immensely helped in the reduction of wasteland in spatio-temporal dimension, by the processes of afforestation, reclamation of marshy, desert and sandy diaras, etc. With the increasing population, even the smallest amount of wasteland left is pinching because it could give sustenance to our society if its no-use or misuse could be checked.

Analysis of the Problem

On the marginal areas of forest cover low fertility of land, coarse texture of soil, lesser population density, the menace of wild animals, relatively rugged terrain and soil erosion during the rainy season are some of the determinants responsible for the presence of wasteland in the district of Munger. For example in Jhajha where the forest cover is in 21 per cent of the land and the wasteland covers 32 per cent of the land.

For example, in the anchals of Sheikhpura and Tarapur where the net sown area is 81 per cent and 85 per cent respectively, there is only 1 per cent of wasteland. On the other hand, Munger Sadar, Jhajha and Sono where the wasteland is relatively high 44 per cent, 32 per cent and 30 per cent respectively, there is a net sown area of only 37 per cent, 11 per cent and 20 per cent respectively.

It has been found that in most of the anchals where the development indices are low, the percentage of wasteland is high such as in Munger Sadar and hence it has a wasteland of over 44 per cent of total land especially in flood-affected areas of the riparian tracts of the Ganges.

On the other hand, it has been found that in some of the anchals, the amount of wasteland is low. For example, in Kharagpur, the wasteland in only 10 per cent.

Distribution of Wasteland

In the district of Munger at the time of flood each and every year, the process of alluviation and dilluviation near the Ganges river in the north favours high percentage of wasteland (44% in Munger Sadar), whereas slightly less than this amount of wasteland (32% in Jhajha) is found in the southern part of Munger where the forest-clad hills restrict high amount of cultivated land.

Table 8.1: Anchals in the district of Munger with percentage of land under forest, net sown area and wasteland (1984-85)

Sl. No. Anchals	*% of Forest*	*% of N S A*	*% of wasteland*
1. Jamui	0.04	62	4
2. Khaira	36.79	24	16
3. Sikandra	11.67	42	5
4. Lakshmipur	37.21	54	12
5. Jhajha	21.32	11	32
6. Chakai	41.20	19	18
7. Sono	6.61	20	30
8. Lakhisarai	10.12	56	11
9. Barahiya	–	76	12
10. Surajgarha	22.35	49	12
11. Barbigha	–	86	2
12. Sheikhpura	–	81	1
13. Ariari	–	52	3
14. Halsi	0.20	49	3
15. Sadar	0.10	37	44
16. Jamalpur	7.96	55	16
17. Kharagpur	31.86	43	10
18. Dharhora	54.51	54	1
19. Tarapur	–	85	1
20. Sangrampur	2.75	71	7

Source: Department of Statistics and Evaluation, Munger, 1984-35.

So far as the anchals of Barahiya, Lakhisarai, Surajgarha and Kharagpur are concerned, the wasteland varies from 10 per cent to 16 per cent. In these anchals, the marginal land in between the flood plains of the Ganges in the north, and drought prone hilly areas in the south Munger help in the formation of waterlogged ground of Barahiya and Kabartal each year for 9 months (July to March) resulting in relatively medium high amount of wasteland (12%).

The anchals where 3 per cent to 10 per cent wasteland is found are Sikandra, Ariari, Halsi, Jamui and Kharagpur (1984-85). In all these areas, the amount of wasteland is low due to the wastage of land on hillsides besides the presence of some forest margins.

The anchals where very low amounts (1% to 3%) of wasteland are found are Barbigha, Sheikhpura, Dharhara and Tarapur (11%). All these are the highly developed agricultural sectors of the district of Munger where most of the land is devoted to agricultural operations.

Contributions of Flood and Drought in the Enhancement of Wasteland

The problem of flood and drought is responsible for the permanence of wasteland in the district of Munger. In diara land of the north which is the Ganges riparian tract and in the Barahiya Tal area, the flood havoc is seen each and every year, whereas Jhajha, Chakai and Jamui are the anchals in south Munger, where due to lack of water drought favours high percentage of wasteland. Hence, it is essential to check flood havoc in the north and the construction of river embankment is proceeding along with the completion of Dakranala Project, whereas in the south Munger it is essential to obstruct free flow of water through the construction of reservoirs, mini-dams and regulation of water through irrigation channels.

In the north, the problem of Tal area is similar to the Ganges belt. The total cultivable land in this area is only 1,04,366 hectares and the same amount is going waste. In 1979, the government adopted the project of Tal area reclamation but till now no progress has been made in this direction.

In the drought affected area of Jamui, Chakai and Jhajha, the State Government has adopted a scheme to eradicate the problem of drought in south Munger. Under this scheme deep boring has been done at 313 places along with the energizing of 300 tubewells. As this scheme known as DPAP is not sufficient to solve the problem, there is need for coordination between the activities of farmers and the government especially in the field of irrigation, livestock rearing, construction of road and providing the facility of electricity, because these are essential components for regional integrated development[7] and will help in reducing the amount of wasteland.

Reclamation of Wasteland

In reclaiming the wasteland for agricultural purposes, the improvement in surface drainage, checking soil erosion, removing waterlogging from the ground besides improving the conditions of alkali and acidic soils are essential in order to change the soil characteristics.

Drainage is the removal of surplus water from the soil whether by natural or artificial means. The lands which require drainage are: heavy clay soils from which rainwater cannot drain easily; low-lying flat areas surrounded by hills; land with little slope and with an impervious sub-soil; delta land at the mouth of rivers and swamps, marshes and jhils. Wastelands of all these characteristics are found in Tal area.

The prevention of soil erosion is recognized as most important for developing agriculture. The soil erosion may be of two types: sheet wash erosion over a large area during a flood and speedy flow of river water; and gully erosion which produces gullies. It may be prevented by a ground cover, such as grass of some kind, a cover crop, bunding, the mulch spray such as organic refuse, and sometimes deep ploughing. In areas where rocks are plentiful, gully erosion may be further prevented by filling in the gully at intervals with rocks.

Other measures may be adopted as the modification in the prevailing land use, restriction of animal grazing on the slopy ground, weakening of streams' flow, practice terrace farming besides afforestation, construction of flood protective embankments along the rivers and adopting other flood control measures.

Canclusion

The wasteland development programme in India has been given national priority in order to protect environment from pollution. This can be effected by planting trees which could provide fodder to the animals and firewood to people voluntary organization and school children should be invited to help accomplish the task.

Wasteland produces much below its potential, and the area is increasing each year at an alarming rate.

It is hoped that the establishment of a National Wastelands Development Board would promote policies, strategies, and structures for afforestation, for the basic subsistence needs of fuelwood and fodder, and working in collaboration with peoples' agencies.

Wastelands are aboundantly found in the flood-prone areas, forest margins besides public land for which there is no proprietary right to anybody. In case the wastelands are not bad lands they are utilized as grazing lands. They need careful identification, inquiry, classification, conservation and planning for proper reclamation.

NOTES

1. *Readings in Land Utilization*, The Indian Society of Agricultural Economics, Bombay, 1957, p. 231.
2. S.N. Singh, "Distribution and Changing Pattern of Cultivable Wastes in Kerakat Tehsil, Jaunpur District, U.P.", *National Geographical Journal of India*, Vol. XV, Nos. 3 & 4, 1969, pp. 207-223.
3. A.B. Mukherji, "Geographical Patterns of Changes in Agricultural Wastelands in Uttar Pradesh", *Geographical Review of India*, Vol. XXXII, No. 2, 1971, pp. 120-132.
4. J. Singh, "Agricultural Colonization of Cultivable Wasteland in India", *Deccan Geographer*, Vol. IX, No. 2, 1971, pp. 135-149.
5. A.L. Singh, "Time Distribution and Utilization of Uncultivated Lands in Kohli Tehsil", *Geographical Review of India*, Vol. XXXIX, No. 3, 1977, pp. 206-211.
6. S. Pandey, "Changing Pattern of Cultivable Waste in Pharenda Tehsil (U.P.), *Uttar Bharat Bhugol Patrika*, Vol. XLLI, No. 1 & 2, 1977, pp. 35-44.
7. U.P. Sinha (1985). *Planned Development of Resources in a Developing Region*, Inter India Publications, New Delhi, pp. 245-46.

9

Wasteland in Uttar Pradesh: An Analysis of its Pattern, Growth and Strategy for Future Development

S. C. Srivastava and *Banwari Lal*

Introduction

Land as a factor of production is very peculiar since it possesses some important features which distinguish it from other factors of production. Land is a free gift of nature, while others are man-made. It, therefore, follows that we have to accept it as it is.

The significance of land is because of the multi-dimensional use which it is put to. Land supplies space for economic and other operations, and it is required for all the activities whether they are related to primary sector, secondary sector or tertiary sector. Everything that we use can be traced ultimately to land. Life without land is inconceivable. However, in a State like Uttar Pradesh, where 74.5 per cent of the population earns its livelihood from agriculture, this inelastic and invaluable asset holds the key to rural and agrarian prosperity.

The total reporting area of the State is 297.6 lakh hects. and the arable land is about 192 lakh hects. while the scope for increasing agricultural production through expansion of existing net area sown of about 173 lakh hects. is limited due to increasing demand for non-agricultural uses as highways, reservoirs, industry, urban expansion, etc. The demand for food and other agricultural products is also increasing fast due to an increase in both per capita income and population. In such a situation, the State economy cannot afford to have any amount of wasteland. Facing the tremendous challenge of poverty, particularly rural poverty, the economy will have to find ways and means to put its every patch of land under most judicious and optimum use.

Although wasteland in its different forms has been in existence since long, its conceptualization on scientific lines is only of recent origin. Comprehensive studies, particularly at the regional level, are lacking which could throw sufficient light on the concept, causes, identification of wastelands, etc. This calls for making intensive and scientific studies of identification, and classification of wasteland as also its growth and pattern, which could provide a basis for adopting sound land policies and programmes. The present chapter seeks to deal with these important aspects of wasteland.

The nature has gifted land with unique life sustaining potential, which has made it invaluable and indispensable for various ecological and economic needs. But during the course of time, on account of a number of factors, some lands became degraded and unworthy of performing these vital functions. These tracks of lands are termed as wasteland. It may broadly be categorized into culturable wasteland and unculturable wasteland. The former lands although unsuitable for agriculture possess the potential of being developed for vegetation cover while the latter do not have even this potential. While gullied or ravinous lands, undulating lands, surface waterlogged land and marsh, salt-affected lands and degraded forest lands form the category of culturable wastelands, barren rocky areas and snow covered areas come under unculturable wasteland.

Studies tracing the reason behind land converting into wastelands indicate both natural and man-made factors involved in the process. Without going into details of various reasons, it would suffice here to mention that, broadly, sheet erosion, wind erosion, stream erosion, waterlogging, salinity and alkalinity, stuff cultivation, sand dune movement, etc., have been found as the main contributing factors.

At the country level mainly two organizations, *viz.* National Bureau of Soil Survey and Land Use Planning, Nagpur, of the Indian Council of Agricultural Research and All India Soil and Land Use Survey of the Department of Agriculture are engaged in performing the task of collecting and analysing the data on wastelands. Recently, a National

Wasteland Development Board has also been established by the Government of India. However, at the State level, data on land use is maintained by the Department of Agriculture on the old pattern in 10 different classifications with no specific category of "Wasteland". So, while one can find a sound data base of wasteland at the national level, it is in a rudimentary form at the regional level. The available data on land use will have to be classified as per definition and categorization of wasteland standardized by the Government of India. In the State of Uttar Pradesh, a high power committee headed by the Agriculture Production Commissioner comprising all the concerned secretaries and heads of departments of the government has been established for the review and monitoring of wasteland. Now, the authentic and precise data on wasteland are well expected to be maintained on an all-India pattern.

Trend and Pattern

In the limitations of required data on wasteland as already indicated, we have, in the present context, treated areas under : (i) barren and unculturable waste, (ii) culturable waste, and (iii) permanent pastures and other grazing land as wasteland. We have culled out figures from Agricultural Records, in respect of each of these categories for a period of 33 years from 1950-51 to 1983-84 for the analysis of the trend and pattern of wasteland in Uttar Pradesh. The analysis of land use pattern and thereafter of trend and pattern of wasteland has been carried out both for the state as also for its five economic regions.

Land Use

Land utilization statistics from 1950-51 to 1983-84 presented in Table 9.1 and that of growth rates in Table 9.2 provide sufficient insight into the trend and pattern of land use for different purposes. The total reporting area of the State for 1950-51 was 292.58 lakh hects. but in 1983-84 it has been estimated at 297.59 lakh hects. with slight variations in between. The area under forest was about 32 lakh hects. in 1950-51 which increased to about 38 lakh hects. in 1960-61, 49 lakh hects. in 1970-71, 51 lakh hects. in 1980-81 and was almost the same in 1983-84. In terms of growth rates, the area under forest shows an increase of 1.74 per cent during the decade 1950-51 to 1960-61, 2.70 per cent during 1960-61 to 1970-71 and 0.37 per cent during 1970-71 to 1980-81. An increasing trend is visible in the area put to cultivation and that under non-agricultural uses. The former increased from 18.5 lakh hects in 1950-51 to 23.5 lakh hects. in 1983-84. The corresponding figures for the latter are 37.3 lakh hects. and 77.9 lakh hects. This is quite obvious because of an increase in human and animal population. Similarly, area under "permanent pastures" and "other fallow land" exhibited a rising trend over the years. The area under "current fallow" shows a marked decline in the initial years but it appears to follow a rising behaviour. In the remaining categories of land, *viz.* barren and "unculturable waste" and "miscellaneous trees and groves" depict a declining trend.

The pattern of land use that emerges from the data is indeed interesting and encouraging. While the area under barren and unculturable waste has decreased, the land put to non-agricultural uses, such as roads, rail lines, ponds, playgrounds, schools, hospitals, reservoirs, dams, canals, industry, etc., has gone up. This shows efforts towards putting wasteland to some productive activities. Decrease in the area of culturable waste and increase in the forest area is yet another happy observation, which is quite necessary for maintaining an ecological balance. A successive increase in the "net area sown" and the "land under permanent pastures and other grazing land" is quite compatible with rising human and animal population.

Land use data for different economic regions (Table 9.4 and 9.5 of respective regions) show that the Eastern Region accounted for about 29.2 per cent of the total reporting area of State in 1983-84 followed by the Western Region (27.6%), Hill Region (17.9%), Central Region (15.4%) and Bundelkhand Region (9.9%). With insignificant variations, their respective proportions were similar in 1950-51 as well.

Among the five economic regions, Hill region has the lion's share in the area under forest (about 6.4%). However, forest area in all the regions has increased from 1950-51 till 1970-71. Therefore, forest area has become almost constant. The area under current fallow decreased in 1983-84 as compared to 1950-51 in the case of Hill and Bundelkhand regions while a reverse trend is found in the case of Eastern and Central Regions. In the Western Region, it has remained almost at the same level. As regards net area sown, except the Hill Region, where it has a declining trend, all other regions show an overall increasing trend in the period under analysis.

Wasteland

As pointed out earlier, wasteland in the present analysis comprises "barren and unculturable waste", "culturable waste" and "permanent pastures". Relevant figures indicating the trend of wasteland in Uttar Pradesh may also be seen in Table 9.4 and 9.5 referred to earlier.

The magnitude of wasteland in the State was about 52 lakh hects. in 1950-51 which consistently decreased over the year and by the year 1983-84 it reduced to less than half (25 lakh hects). In terms of percentage to total reporting area, the wasteland accounted for about 17.8 per cent on the eve of the First Plan and 8.5 per cent in the penultimate year of the Sixth Plan. Its two components, *viz.* "barren and unculturable waste" and "cultivable waste" depict the same trend. However, the declining trend in the farmer is more steeper than that of the latter. In 1950-51, their respective areas were about 29 lakh hects. and 23 lakh hects. but in 1983-84 land in both the categories was almost at the same level being about 11 lakh hects. The third component, i.e. "permanent pastures" shows an increasing trend. In 1955-56, it was found to be only 0.1 per cent of the reporting area whereas in 1983-84 it was exactly one per cent.

Looking to the growth rate statistics, it is noticed that wasteland registered maximum decrease in the decade 1960-61 to 1970-71 with an annual rate of 4 per cent, which was mainly due to a corresponding significant decline in land under barren and unculturable waste. It decreased at annual rate of nearly 6 per cent. However, negative growth recorded by the category of "culturable waste" in all the three decades ending in 1960-61, 1970-71 and 1980-81 and thereafter also indicate a very consistent declining growth trend.

Looking at the wasteland figures for different regions of the State, it is noticed that all the five regions indicate almost a similar trend as in the case of the State as a whole. However, it is important to note the Hill Region alone accounts for about one-third area of the total wasteland in the State. The remaining four economic regions, *viz.* Western, Eastern, Central and Bundelkhand, shared almost equally. Their share ranged between about 13 per cent and 18 per cent. Another significant feature is observed with regard to composition of wasteland, which shows variation among the regions. The area under culturable waste was higher than the area under barren and unculturable waste in the beginning of the period under analysis in the case of the Eastern, Western and Central Regions but the situation reversed by the end of the period. In the Bundelkhand Region, area under both the categories depicts consistent decline throughout but the former maintained the lead over the latter. In the case of the Hill Region also, while a declining trend is discernible in the category of land under "culturable waste" follows this trend up to 1970-71 but, thereafter, it shows a sharp rising trend so much so that its share (5.92%) in the total reporting area surpassed that of the former (5.42%) by the year 1983-84 against their respective shares, 1.79 per cent and 28.29 per cent in 1950-51.

An analysis of decadal growth rates of all the three components of wasteland for different regions, contained in relevant tables, revealed the same behaviour but in a more pronounced manner.

Earlier Efforts

Limitations of availability of specific and precise data on wasteland have already been pointed out. In the absence of relevant data, it was found difficult to review the efforts made in the direction of developing wasteland. In the present situation, there is hardly any concrete idea about the total magnitude of wasteland in the State as such. However, it needs mention that whatever efforts have been made to develop wasteland were made by the Forest and Agriculture Departments of the State Government. Their activity relates to reclamation of usar and ravine lands and afforestation of degraded lands. The Agriculture Department has reclaimed 0.11 million hects. of usar land till 1985-86. Similarly, about 42,000 hects. ravinous area has been protected till 1985-86. Since the organization for the development of wasteland has come into existence in the State, it is expected that development efforts for wastelands would be suitably and substantially enhanced.

Projected Land Use Pattern in A.D. 2000

The total reporting area is almost constant in the State as shown in Table 9.1.

Table 9.1 : Reporting Area at a Few Points of Time

Year	*Reporting Area (in lakh hects)*
1950-51	292.58
1960-61	294.95
1970-71	298.06
1980-81	297.39
1983-84	297.59

It is evident from Table 9.1 that the reporting area, during the span of more than three decades, has almost been constant showing an increase of about 1.6 per cent. It, therefore, follows that there is hardly any possibility of increasing the reporting area to any appreciable extent. It may, thus, be assumed that the reporting area for the perspective period ending A.D. 2000 would be of the order of 298 lakh hects., the highest area reported in 1970-71.

The existing area under forest is not desirable in view of the fact that the area under forest is already much less than recommended for maintaining the ecological balance. There is, thus, an imperative need to increase the area under trees and forests. According to the National Forest Policy norms for a proper ecological balance in the nature, about 33.3 per cent of the entire area in the State should be covered under forest. It does not seem feasible to obtain this yardstick in U.P. However, efforts will be made to increase the area under forest as such as practicable. This area may be diverted from wasteland.

The land under permanent pastures and other grazing lands was about 1 per cent of the reporting area. This area is appropriate, according to the present situation and other constraints. This area may be kept at 1 per cent of the reporting area even in future, but the pressing need is to maintain these pastures and grazing lands in their true sense. Practically these grazing lands no more have grass. If these grazing lands are properly developed and maintained, the requirements of animals in future with this land could be met.

The land under miscellaneous tree crops and groves not included in net area sown may be taken as more or less the same as exists at present. In 1983-84, its area was 1.84 per cent to reporting area which slipped down from 4.84 per cent as observed in 1950-51. The average area under this category for the period 1980-81 to 1983-84 worked out to be 1.98 per cent. So, the area under this category may be assumed to be about 2 per cent in the terminal year (A.D. 2000).

Land put to non-agricultural uses has a direct link with the population. As the population increases, the land put to non-agricultural uses also increases. This fact has been observed in the last 33 years also. Table 9.2 gives the area put to non-agricultural use against the corresponding population at a few points of time.

Assuming a linear relationship between population and land put to non-agricultural uses an area of about 28 lakh hects. under non-agricutural uses was arrived at corresponding to a population of 1,700 lakhs as estimated for the year A.D. 2000, the area put. to non-agricultural uses is projected to increase by 1.73 per cent as compared to 1980-81.

Table 9.2 : Population and Area under Non-agricultural Uses

Year	*Population (in lakhs)*	*Area put to non-agricultural uses (in lakh hects.)*
1950-51	632	18.53
1960-61	737	19.12
1970-71	883	20.34
1980-81	1109	22.80

The possibility of diverting land is obviously from the following categories of land:

1. Barren (including usar) and unculturable land;
2. Culturable waste;
3. Current fallows; and
4. Other fallows.

In order to meet our foodgrain requirements in A.D. 2000, it is proposed to increase area under cultivation. Most of the increase in area would come from barren and unculturable land, culturable waste and fallow lands. Although, the additional foodgrain requirements will be met by increasing the net cultivated area, the total area is limited and there is hardly any possibility of bringing more and more area under plough. The desired level of production is to be achieved by increasing the area sown more than once and by increasing the yield per hectare. Some basic changes in the cropping pattern have to be introduced, which will lead to the replacement of low yielding crops by high yielding crops. The envisaged cropping pattern for the year A.D. 2000 largely takes into account the high potentiality of the high yielding varieties of rice and wheat. The area under these two cereals has been envisaged to increase substantially while the area under crops like small millets to diminish considerably. As regards the area under pulses, a considerable increase in production has to be achieved for meeting the growing demands of pulses and this increase in production has to be largely achieved by increasing the area, as unlike rice and wheat advanced scientific technology has yet to be developed for pulses. If some high yielding varieties of pulses could be evolved, which may respond well to fertilizers and may be free from pests and diseases, the additional demand for pulses can be met by a smaller area.

As stated earlier, the increase in area under forests area put to non-agricultural uses and under cultivation may be brought from barren and unculturable land, culturable waste and fallow land. If the year 1980-81 is taken as the base point, it is proposed to reduce the area of barren and unculturable land from 3.84 per cent to 2 per cent in A.D. 2000 and put under forests and the remaining portion will be put to non-agricultural uses. Similarly, the area of culturable waste has to be reduced from 3.86 per cent to 1.90 per cent. This area will go to forests. The area under cultivation (net area sown) will be increased by reducing fallow land.

With all considerations and requirements of future as discussed above the projected land use pattern by A.D. 2000 is shown in Table 9.3.

As shown is Table 9.3, the area under forest is about 62.58 lakh hects., i.e. about 21 per cent of the reporting area. According to the National Forest Policy norm, the area under forest should be about 33.3 per cent of the reporting area. So in the proposed pattern, a provision of 21 per cent is envisaged which does not include the area of land near

Table 9.3 : Projected land use Pattern of U.P. in A.D. 2000

Sl. No.	*Item*	*Projected area in A.D. 2000 (in lakh hects.)*	*% contribution to reporting area*
1.	Forests	62.58	21.00
2.	Barren and unculturable land	5.96	2.00
3.	Land put to non-agricultural uses	28.01	9.40
4.	Culturable waste	5.66	1.90
5.	Permanent pastures and other grazing land	2.98	1.00
6.	Land under misc. tree crops and groves not included in net area sown	5.96	2.00
7.	Current fallows	6.56	2.20
8.	Other fallows	5.96	2.00
9.	Net area sown	174.33	58.50
	Total	**298.00**	**100.00**

roads covered under social forestry. Taking into account the area covered under social forestry too, the national norm for forest area will be well-nigh achieved. The area under wasteland would also reduce from 25.33 per cent of the total area in 1983-84 to 14.60 per cent in A.D. 2000.

Strategy

An appropriate strategy for the smooth and speedy execution of an activity emanates from set goals, prevailing situations, conditions and processes. In the present context, it appears logical to run through these aspects in brief prior to framing of specific strategies. The wasteland development activity aims at soil conservation, improvement of environment, balancing ecosystem, etc. The micro-level targets are to be derived from these macro and long-term goals of wasteland development. As regards reasons for wastelands, it may be reiterated that it occurs due to water erosion, which includes sheet erosion, ravines, riverines, waterlogging and gully erosion. Wastelands are also caused on account of wind erosion comprising shifting of sand dunes, extra moisture and coastal dunes as also because of salinity and alkalinity. Of the total wasteland (non-forest area) under saline and alkaline lands and water eroded area for the country as estimated by the Society for Promotion of Wastelands Development, the State of Uttar Pradesh accounts for about 18 per cent and 7 per cent in these two respective categories.

It would be relevant to indicate the broad implications of degradation of our land resources. The loss in forest cover alone is estimated at 1.5 million hectares per year. Consequences of depletion of forest cover are extremely serious. The loss of forest wealth is the first direct effect. The second is large scale erosion of top soil. The third is the degeneration of existing agricultural land. The fourth is the increasing havoc caused by floods. Obviously, all other consequences in the form of increased poverty and deteriorated quality of life follow the loss of top soil. It has been estimated that it takes anything between 500 and 1,000 years to create one inch of top soil. Reestablishing lost forest cover to full maturity may take between 50 and 100 years.

Contributing factors towards deforestation and degradation of land resources have been observed as increase in human and animal population, forest fires, pressure from industry, railways, building of dams, reservoirs, roads, bad agricultural practices, bad irrigation, shifting cultivation, etc.

In view of the above background, the core strategy that emerges to cope up with the major ecological and socio-economic crisis is as follows:

(i) Approach towards halting the depletion of our invaluable natural resources will have to be protective, regenerative and productive. The present degradation of land must be protected from further damage and what has been lost must also be regenerated. At the same time, support capacity must be increased to enable a growing population to live a better life. The productive measures will have to be taken simultaneously with protective and regenerative steps.

(ii) The foremost step in the context of translating the three pronged strategy into reality is the immediate identification of the nature and magnitude of wastelands not only for the State as a whole but also for its micro-planning, units, *viz.* districts and blocks.

(iii) A programme for wastelands development has been

launched with utmost zeal, fervour and expectations. It is very much appreciated in view of the seriousness of the problem. However, for the sure success of the programme, no stone should be left unturned to make it a people's movement lest the poor folk be by-passed like in many other programmes wherein benefits have largely gone to rich and influential people.

(iv) A target of bringing 5 million hectares of land every year under fuelwood and fodder plantations has been set out for the country. It appears an ambitious target but at the same time an unavoidable necessity. This implies, therefore, new initiative, new structure and of course a determined reorientation in our thinking and policies.

(v) For the achievement of the target, saplings would be needed in good quantity. For the sake of involvement of more and more people in the programme, nurseries need to be decentralized in the people's sector and marginal farmers, schools and women's groups should be encouraged and helped to develop such nurseries.

(vi) If a people's programme is to be ushered in, 'single roof' concept will have to be introduced whereby all related questions of leasing land, credit and other inputs and market information, etc., are dealt with.

(vii) Publicity of the wasteland development programme has to be wider and effective to make people adequately aware of its contents.

(viii) Considering the financial limitation on the part of the rural poor to invest, it would be desirable to integrate NREP/RLEGP with the wasteland development programme.

(ix) Tree growers' cooperatives comprising small and marginal farmers and landless labourers may be formed to accelerate the programme as these cooperatives have shown impressive results in the State of Gujarat and Maharashtra.

(x) Involvement of voluntary agencies to undertake wastelands' development appears quite necessary both on protective and productive grounds.

Table 9.4: Land utilization statistics of State of Uttar Pradesh (in lakh hects.)

Sl.No.	Land Use Category	1950-51	1955-56	1960-61	1965-66	1970-71	1971-72	1972-73	1973-74	1974-75
1	2	3	4	5	6	7	8	9	10	11
1.	Reporting area	292.58	301.03	294.95	294.30	298.06	299.17	297.83	298.26	298.62
2.	Forest	31.94	42.71	37.94	37.76	49.53	50.37	50.12	51.31	51.29
		(10.92)	(14.19)	(12.86)	(12.83)	(16.62)	(16.84)	(16.03)	(17.20)	(17.18)
3.	Barren and	28.87	26.00	25.91	25.15	14.18	14.18	14.17	12.23	12.22
	uncultivable waste	(9.87)	(8.64)	(8.78)	(8.55)	(4.76)	(4.74)	(4.76)	(4.10)	(4.09)
4.	Land put to	18.53	18.45	19.12	19.88	20.34	20.33	20.31	21.20	21.44
	non-agricultural uses	(6.33)	(6.13)	(6.48)	(6.75)	(6.82)	(6.80)	(6.82)	(7.11)	(7.18)
5.	Culturable	23.11	18.24	16.40	14.89	13.45	13.25	13.06	15.58	15.36
	waste	(7.90)	(6.06)	(5.56)	(5.06)	(4.51)	(4.43)	(4.39)	(5.22)	(5.14)
6.	Permanent	N.A.	0.33	0.44	0.66	0.77	0.78	0.78	2.78	2.79
	pastures		(0.11)	(0.15)	(0.22)	(0.26)	(0.26)	(0.26)	(0.93)	(0.93)
7.	Misc. trees	14.15	11.92	8.93	8.11	12.60	12.57	12.51	7.94	7.91
	and groves	(4.84)	(3.96)	(3.03)	(2.76)	(4.23)	(4.20)	(4.11)	(2.66)	(2.65)
8.	Current	10.78	1.91	1.74	8.94	8.70	8.98	9.27	9.12	9.01
	fallow	(3.68)	(0.63)	(0.59)	(3.04)	(2.92)	(3.00)	(3.11)	(3.06)	(3.01)
9.	Other fallow	2.91	12.81	12.60	5.48	5.45	5.54	5.63	6.42	6.97
	lands	(0.99)	(4.25)	(4.27)	(1.86)	(1.83)	(1.85)	(1.89)	(2.15)	(2.23)
10.	Net area sown	162.31	168.93	171.88	173.43	173.05	173.17	171.94	171.68	171.61
		(55.48)	(56.02)	(58.27)	(58.93)	(58.06)	(57.88)	(57.73)	(57.56)	(57.47)
11.	Area sown	37.29	41.50	45.42	47.31	59.02	57.07	57.33	58.39	57.69
	more than once	(12.75)	(13.78)	(15.40)	(16.07)	(19.80)	(19.08)	(19.25)	(19.58)	(19.32)
12.	Total cropped	199.60	210.13	217.30	220.74	232.07	230.24	229.27	230.07	229.30
	area	(68.22)	(69.80)	(73.67)	(75.00)	(77.86)	(76.96)	(76.98)	(77.14)	(76.79)
13.	Wasteland	51.98	44.57	42.75	40.70	28.40	28.21	28.01	30.59	30.37
		(17.77)	(14.81)	(14.49)	(13.83)	(9.53)	(9.43)	(9.41)	(10.25)	10.16)

Table 9.4: *(Contd.)*

Sl. No.	*Land Use Category*	*1975-76*	*1976-77*	*1977-78*	*1978-79*	*1979-80*	*1980-81*	*1981-82*	*1982-83*	*1983-84*
1	*2*	*12*	*13*	*14*	*15*	*16*	*17*	*18*	*19*	*20*
1.	Reporting Area	298.48	297.86	297.95	298.09	297.46	297.39	297.09	297.48	297.59
2.	Forest	51.41	50.75	51.13	51.09	51.19	51.29	51.96	51.20	51.21
		(17.22)	(17.04)	(17.16)	(17.14)	(17.21)	(17.25)	(17.25)	(17.21)	(17.21)
3.	Barren and un-cultivable waste	12.13	11.92	11.53	11.47	11.65	11.41	11.21	11.20	11.06
		(4.06)	(4.00)	(3.87)	(3.85)	(3.92)	(3.84)	(3.77)	(3.76)	(3.72)
4.	Land put to non-agricultural uses	21.62	21.64	21.79	22.18	22.43	22.80	23.22	23.36	23.51
		(7.24)	(7.27)	(7.31)	(7.44)	(7.54)	(7.67)	(7.82)	(7.85)	(7.90)
5.	Culturable waste	14.93	14.23	13.77	13.38	11.84	11.48	11.22	11.47	11.29
		(5.00)	(4.78)	(4.62)	(4.49)	(3.98)	(3.86)	(3.78)	(3.86)	(3.79)
6.	Permanent pastures	2.79	2.77	2.76	2.98	2.99	2.95	2.97	2.99	2.98
		(0.93)	(0.93)	(0.93)	(1.00)	(1.01)	(0.99)	(1.00)	(1.01)	(1.00)
7.	Misc trees and groves	7.91	7.85	7.78	6.79	6.65	6.39	5.99	5.68	5.49
		(2.65)	(2.64)	(2.61)	(2.28)	(2.24)	(2.15)	(2.01)	(1.91)	(1.84)
8.	Current fallow	9.62	8.93	9.08	9.32	14.15	11.70	10.99	11.76	11.59
		(3.22)	(3.00)	(3.05)	(3.13)	(4.76)	(3.93)	(3.70)	(3.95)	(3.89)
9.	Other fallow lands	9.05	6.02	5.90	6.07	6.58	7.16	7.34	7.56	7.73
		(2.03)	(2.02)	(1.98)	(2.04)	(2.21)	(2.41)	(2.47)	(2.54)	(2.61)
10.	Net area sown	172.01	173.75	174.21	174.81	169.98	172.21	172.89	172.26	172.73
		(57.63)	(58.33)	(58.47)	(58.64)	(57.14)	(57.91)	(58.19)	(57.91)	(58.04)
11.	Area sown more than once	58.97	57.77	59.28	68.19	66.44	73.53	74.85	74.82	77.94
		(19.76)	(19.40)	(19.90)	(22.88)	(22.34)	(24.73)	(25.19)	(25.15)	(26.19)
12.	Total cropped area	230.98	231.52	233.49	243.00	236.42	245.74	247.74	247.08	250.67
		(77.39)	(77.73)	(78.37)	(81.52)	(79.48)	(82.64)	(83.38)	(83.06)	(84.23)
13.	Waste land	29.85	28.92	28.06	27.83	26.48	25.84	25.40	25.66	25.33
		(9.99)	(9.71)	(9.42)	(9.34)	(8.91)	(8.69)	(8.56)	(8.63)	(8.51)

Note: Bracketed figures denote percentage to total reporting area.

Table 9.4 A: Land utilisation statistics of Eastern Region of U.P. (in lakh hects.)

Sl. No.	*Land Use Category*	*1950-51*	*1955-56*	*1960-61*	*1965-66*	*1970-71*	*1971- 72*	*1972-73*	*1973-74*	*1974-75*
1	2	3	4	5	6	7	8	9	10	11
1.	Reporting area	85.00	88.26	86.10	84.96	87.38	NA	87.59	NA	87.82
2.	Forest	3.88 (4.56)	8.11 (9.19)	6.71 (7.79)	5.76 (6.78)	8.48 (9.70)	NA	8.54 (9.75)	NA	8.52 (9.70)
3.	Barren and unculti-vable waste	4.12 (4.85)	3.20 (3.63)	3.21 (3.73)	3.03 (3.57)	2.89 (3.31)	NA	(2.87) (3.28)	NA	(2.98) (3.39)
4.	Land put to non-agri-cultural uses	7.02 (8.26)	6.88 (7.80)	7.20 (8.56)	7.27 (8.56)	7.35 (8.41)	NA	7.38 (8.43)	NA	7.56 (8.60)
5.	Culturable waste	6.75 (7.94)	5.12 (5.80)	4.86 (5.64)	4.43 (5.21)	3.96 (4.53)	NA	3.88 (4.43)	NA	3.78 (4.30)
6.	Permanent pastures	NA	0.13 (0.15)	0.12 (0.14)	0.09 (0.11)	0.14 (0.16)	NA	0.14 (0.16)	NA	0.17 (0.19)
7.	Misc. trees and groves	4.85 (5.71)	4.89 (5.54)	3.02 (3.51)	2.79 (3.28)	2.85 (3.26)	NA	2.85 (3.25)	NA	288 (328)
8.	Current fallow	3.34 (3.93)	0.19 (0.22)	0.22 (0.26)	2.36 (2.78)	2.30 (2.63)	NA	2.65 (3.03)	NA	2.45 (2.79)
9.	Other fallow lands	0.83 (0.98)	4.06 (4.60)	4.14 (4.81)	1.92 (2.26)	1.96 (2.24)	NA	1.91 (2.18)	NA	2.29 (2,61)
10.	Net area sown	54.21 (63.78)	55.68 (63.09)	56.62 (65.76)	57.32 (67.47)	57.44 (65.74)	NA	57.38 (65.51)	NA	57.19 (65.50)
11.	Area sown more than once	16.03 (18.86)	17.10 (19.37)	17.94 (20.84)	18.58 (21.87)	19.54 (22.36)	NA	18.09 (20 65)	NA	20.33 (23.15)
12.	Total cropped area	70.24 (82.64)	72.78 (82.46)	74.56 (86.60)	75.90 (89.34)	76.98 (89.10)	NA NA	75.47 (86.16)	NA	77.52 (88.27)
13.	Wasteland % of wasteland to reporting area	10.87 (12.79)	8.45 (9.58)	8.19 (9.51)	7.55 (8.89)	6.99 (8.00)	NA	6.89 (7.87)	NA	6.93 (7.88)

Table 9.4 A: (*Contd.*)

Sl. No.	*Land Use Category*	*1975-76*	*1976-77*	*1977-78*	*1978-79*	*1979-80*	*1980-81*	*1981-82*	*1982-83*	*1983-84*
1	2	12	13	14	15	16	17	18	19	20
1.	Reporting area	87.79	87.60	87.43	86.55	86.41	86.40	86.36	86.64	86.66
2.	Forest	8.53	8.52	8.42	8.35	8.29	8.24	8.26	8.23	8.23
		(9.72)	(9.73)	(9.63)	(9.65)	(9.59)	(9.54)	(9.56)	(9.50)	(9.50)
3.	Barren and Uncul-	3.00	2.80	2.71	2.37	2.42	2.37	2.33	2.33	2.29
	tivable waste	(3.42)	(3.20)	(3.10)	(2.74)	(2.80)	(2.74)	(2.70)	(2.69)	(2.64)
4.	Land put to non-agri	7.60	7.62	7.72	7.86	7.99	8.20	8.46	8.53	8.60
	cultural uses	(8.66)	(8.70)	(8.83)	(9.08)	(9.25)	(9.49)	(9.80)	(9.85)	(9.92)
5.	Culturable waste	3.59	3.36	3.16	2.83	2.35	2.34	2.28	2.30	2.24
		(4.09)	(3.84)	(3.61)	(3.27)	(2.72)	(2.71)	(2.64)	(2.65)	(2.58)
6.	Permanent pasturs	0.17	0.13	0.13	0.16	0.19	0.17	0.18	0.18	0.19
		(0.19)	(0.15)	(0.15)	(0.18)	(0.22)	(0.20)	(0.21)	(0.21)	(0.22)
7.	Misc. trees and	2.87	2.94	2.92	2.54	2.50	2.23	2.01	2.00	1.92
	groves	(3.27)	(3.36)	(3.34)	(2.93)	(2.89)	(2.58)	(2.33)	(2.31)	(2.22)
8.	Current fallow	2.45	2.43	2.63	3.10	4.83	4.11	4.00	4.30	4.24
		(2.79)	(2.77)	(3.01)	(3.58)	(5.59)	(4.76)	(4.63)	(4.96)	(4.89)
9.	Other fallow lands	2.40	1.98	1.96	2.00	2.23	2.24	2.42	2.55	2.71
		(2.32)	(2.26)	(2.24)	(2.32)	(2.58)	(2.59)	(2.80)	(2.94)	(3.13)
10.	Net area sown	57.52	57.82	57.78	57.34	56.61	56.50	56.42	56.22	56.24
		(65.52)	(66.00)	(66.09)	(66.25)	(64.36)	(65.39)	(65.33)	(64.89)	(64.90)
11.	Area sown more	19.49	19.33	20.25	23.47	22.06	25.54	27.47	25.97	26.79
	than once	(22.20)	(22.07)	(23.16)	(27.12)	(25.53)	(29.56)	(31.81)	(29.97)	(30.91)
12.	Total cropped area	77.01	77.15	78.03	80.81	77.67	82.04	83.89	82.19	83.03
		(87.72)	(88.07)	(89.25)	(93.37)	(89.89)	(94.95)	(97.14)	(94.86)	(95.81)
13.	Wasteland % of waste	6.76	6.29	6.00	5.36	4.96	4.88	4.79	4.81	4.72
	land reporting area	(7.70)	(7.19)	(6.86)	(6.19)	(5.74)	(5.65)	(5.55)	(5.55)	(5.44)

Note: Bracketed figures denote percentages to total reporting area.

Table 9.4B : Land utilization statistics of Western Region of U.P. (in lakh hects.)

Sl. No.	*Land Use Category*	*1950-51*	*1955-56*	*1960-61*	*1965-66*	*1970-71*	*1971-72*	*1972-73*	*1973-74*	*1974-75*
1	*2*	*3*	*4*	*5*	*6*	*7*	*8*	*9*	*10*	*11*
1.	Reporting Area	82.22	84.98	83.42	83.23	82.55	NA	81.89	NA	82.48
2.	Forest	1.65 (2.01)	5.22 (6.14)	4.00 (4.80)	4.03 (4.84)	3.73 (4.52)	NA	3.83 (4.68)	NA	3.85 (4.67)
3.	Barren and uncultiv-able waste	4.96 (6.03)	4.05 (4.77)	4.02 (4.82)	3.77 (4.53)	3.46 (4.19)	NA	3.42 (4.18)	NA	3.35 (4.06)
4.	Land put to non-agri cultural uses	5.60 (6.81)	5.67 (6.67)	5.94 (7.12)	6.50 (7.81)	6.81 (8.25)	NA	6.77 (8.27)	NA	6.98 (8.46)
5.	Culturable waste	6.06 (7.37)	4.34 (5.11)	3.90 (4.68)	3.43 (4.12)	3.15 (3.82)	NA	2.93 (3.58)	NA	2.81 (3.41)
6.	Permanent pastures	NA	0.03 (0.04)	0.08 (0.10)	0.22 (0.26)	0.25 (0.30)	NA	0.26 (0.32)	NA	0.27 (0.33)
7.	Misc. trees and Groves	2.79 (3.39)	1.86 (2.19)	1.48 (1.77)	1.21 (1.45)	1.19 (1.44)	NA	1.17 (1.43)	NA	1.16 (1.41)
8.	Current fallow	2.96 (3.60)	1.11 (1.31)	0.93 (1.11)	3.08 (3.70)	2.86 (3.46)	NA	3.08 (3.76)	NA	2.53 (3.07)
9.	Other fallow lands	0.42 (0.51)	3.17 (3.73)	3.29 (3.94)	1.16 (1.39)	1.28 (1.55)	NA	1.18 (1.44)	NA	1.19 (2.32)
10.	Net area sown	57.79 (70.29)	59.53 (70.05)	59.85 (71.75)	59.83 (71.89)	59.83 (72.35)	NA	59.25 (72.35)	NA	59.62 (72.28)
11.	Area sown more than once	12.74 (15.50)	14.68 (17.27)	16.19 (19.41)	16.87 (20.27)	23.57 (28.55)	NA	23.14 (28.26)	NA	23.17 (28.09)
12.	Total cropped area	70.53 (85.79)	74.21 (87.37)	76.04 (91.15)	76.70 (92.15)	83.40 (101.03)	NA	82.39 (100.61)	NA	23.17 (100.38)
13.	Wasteland % of wasteland to reporting area	11.02 (13.40)	8.42 (9.92)	8.00 (9.60)	7.42 (8.91)	6.86 (8.31)	NA	6.61 (8.08)	NA	6.43 (7.80)

Table 9.4.B: *(Contd...)*

Sl. No.	*Land Use Category*	*1975-76*	*1976-77*	*1977-78*	*1978-79*	*1979-80*	*1980-81*	*1981-82*	*1982-83*	*1983-84*
1	*2*	*12*	*13*	*14*	*15*	*16*	*17*	*18*	*19*	*20*
1.	Reporting Area	82.48	82.42	82.41	82.39	82.13	82.07	82.08	82.05	82.08
2.	Forest	3.85 (4.67)	3.84 (4.66)	3.32 (4.64)	3.82 (4.64)	3.81 (4.64)	3.85 (4.69)	3.84 (4.68)	3.82 (4.66)	3.85 (4.69)
3.	Barren and unculti-vable waste	3.28 (3.98)	3.37 (4.09)	3.11 (3.77)	3.03 (3.68)	3.05 (3.71)	2.93 (3.57)	2.94 (3.46)	2.84 (3.46)	2.78 (3.39)
4.	Land put to non-agri-cultural uses	7.07 (8.57)	7.10 (8.61)	7.12 (8.64)	7.19 (8.73)	7.28 (8.86)	7.33 (8.93)	7.40 (9.02)	7.41 (9.03)	7.46 (9.09)
5.	Culturable waste	2.73 (3.31)	2.54 (3.08)	2.39 (2.90)	2.32 (2.82)	1.97 (2.40)	1.80 (2.19)	1.83 (2.23)	1.82 (2.22)	1.79 (2.18)
6.	Permanent pastures	0.26 (0.32)	0.27 (0.33)	0.26 (0.32)	0.25 (0.30)	0.25 (0.30)	0.24 (0.29)	0.23 (0.28)	0.24 (0.29)	0.24 (0.29)
7.	Misc. trees and groves	1.15 (1.39)	1.07 (1.30)	1.06 (1.29)	0.69 (0.84)	0.62 (0.75)	0.61 (0.74)	0.57 (0.69)	0.53 (0.65)	0.51 (0.62)
8.	Current fallow	3.00 (3.64)	2.60 (3.15)	2.74 (3.32)	2.63 (3.19)	4.27 (5.21)	2.96 (3.62)	2.58 (3.14)	2.73 (3.33)	2.63 (3.20)
9.	Other fallow lands	1.49 (1.81)	1.39 (1.69)	1.41 (1.71)	1.50 (1.82)	1.71 (2.08)	1.94 (2.36)	1.92 (2.34)	1.91 (2.33)	1.99 (2.43)
10.	Net area sown	59.64 (72.31)	60.24 (73.09)	60.50 (73.41)	60.96 (73.99)	59.17 (72.04)	60.41 (73.61)	60.87 (74.16)	60.75 (74.04)	60.83 (74.11)
11.	Area sown more than once	24.73 (29.98)	24.70 (29.97)	24.18 (29.34)	28.61 (34.73)	27.80 (33.85)	30.63 (37.32)	29.81 (36.32)	30.39 (37.04)	32.15 (39.17)
12.	Total cropped area	84.37 (102.29)	84.94 (103.06)	84.68 (102.75)	89.57 (108.12)	86.97 (105.89)	91.04 (110.93)	90.68 (110.48)	91.14 (111.08)	92.98 (113.28)
13.	Wasteland % of wasteland to reporting area	6.27 (7.61)	6.18 (7.50)	5.76 (6.99)	5.60 (6.80)	5.27 (6.41)	4.97 (6.05)	4.90 (5.97)	4.90 (5.97)	4.81 (5.86)

Note: Bracketed figures denote percentages to total reporting area.

Table 9.4 C: Land utilization statistics of Central Region of U.P. (in lakh hects.)

Sl. No.	Land Use Category	1950-51	1955-56	1960-61	1965-66	1970-71	1971-72	1972-73	1973-74	1974-75
1	2	3	4	5	6	7	8	9	10	11
1.	Reporting area	45.97	46.91	46.63	46.76	46.52	NA	46.50	NA	46.41
2.	Forest	1.22 (2.65)	2.42 (5.16)	2.23 (4.78)	2.44 (5.22)	2.46 (5.29)	NA	2.43 (5.23)	NA	2.36 (5.09)
3.	Barren and uncultivable waste	3.17 (6.90)	2.66 (5.67)	2.46 (5.28)	2.27 (4.85)	2.19 (4.71)	NA	2.20 (4.73)	NA	2.14 (4.61)
4.	Land put to non-agricultural uses	4.11 (8.94)	4.05 (8.63)	4.09 (8.77)	4.19 (8.96)	4.23 (9.09)	NA	4.24 (9.12)	NA	4.31 (9.29)
5.	Culturable waste	3.86 (8.40)	3.26 (6.95)	2.97 (6.37)	2.54 (5.43)	2.37 (5.09)	NA	2.30 (4.95)	NA	2.22 (4.78)
6.	Permanent pastures	NA	0.07 (0.15)	0.12 (0.26)	0.27 (0.58)	0.30 (0.64)	NA	0.30 (0.65)	NA	0.30 (0.65)
7.	Misc. trees and groves	3.47 (7.55)	2.54 (5.41)	2.18 (4.68)	1.86 (3.98)	1.67 (3.59)	NA	1.67 (3.59)	NA	1.58 (3.40)
8.	Current fallow	1.83 (3.98)	0.30 (0.64)	0.27 (0.58)	1.85 (3.96)	2.11 (4.54)	NA	2.24 (4.82)	NA	2.36 (5.09)
9.	Other fallow lands	0.27 (0.59)	2.65 (5.65)	2.52 (5.40)	1.03 (2.21)	1.10 (2.36)	NA	1.35 (2.90)	NA	1.35 (2.91)
10.	Net area sown	28.04 (61.00)	28.98 (61.78)	29.78 (63.86)	30.30 (64.80)	30.10 (64.70)	NA	29.79 (64.06)	NA	29.79 (64.19)
11.	Area sown more than once	6.32 (13.75)	7.12 (15.18)	8.04 (17.24)	8.57 (18.33)	9.21 (19.80)	NA	8.71 (18.73)	NA	8.54 (18.40)
12.	Total cropped area	34.36 (74.74)	36.10 (76.76)	37.82 (81.11)	38.87 (83.13)	39.31 (84.50)	NA	37.50 (82.80)	NA	38.33 (82.59)
13.	Wasteland % of waste land of reporting area	7.03 (15.30)	5.99 (12.77)	5.55 (11.91)	5.08 (10.86)	4.86 (10.44)	NA	4.80 (10.33)	NA	4.66 (10.04)

Table 9:4 C: (*Contd.*)

Sl. No.	*Land Use Category*	*1975-76*	*1976-77*	*1977-78*	*1978-79*	*1979-80*	*1980-81*	*1981-82*	*1982-83*	*1983-84*
1	*2*	*12*	*13*	*14*	*15*	*16*	*17*	*18*	*19*	*20*
1.	Reporting Area	46.42	46.39	46.34	46.29	46.01	45.99	45.90	45.92	45.93
2.	Forest	2.35 (5.06)	2.34 (5.04)	2.36 (5.09)	2.38 (5.14)	2.31 (5.02)	2.35 (5.11)	2.36 (5.14)	2.34 (5.10)	2.34 (5.09)
3.	Barren and uncultivable waste	2.10 (4.52)	2.07 (4.46)	2.03 (4.38)	1.83 (3.95)	1.92 (4.17)	1.83 (3.98)	1.82 (3.97)	1.77 (3.85)	1.77 (3.85)
4.	Land put to non-agricultural uses	4.35 (9.37)	4.31 (9.29)	4.34 (9.37)	4.34 (9.38)	4.35 (9.45)	4.41 (9.59)	4.46 (9.72)	4.47 (9.73)	4.47 (9.73)
5.	Culturable waste	2.11 (4.55)	1.88 (4.05)	1.84 (3.97)	1.75 (3.78)	1.45 (3.15)	1.49 (3.24)	1.40 (3.05)	1.44 (3.14)	1.42 (3.09)
6.	Permanent pastures	0.30 (0.65)	0.31 (0.67)	0.30 (0.65)	0.30 (0.65)	0.29 (0.63)	0.27 (0.59)	0.28 (0.61)	0.29 (0.63)	0.28 (0.61)
7.	Misc. trees and groves	1.60 (3.45)	1.57 (3.38)	1.54 (3.32)	1.37 (2.96)	1.25 (2.72)	1.27 (2.76)	1.16 (2.53)	1.07 (2.33)	1.03 (2.24)
8.	Current fallow	2.57 (5.54)	2.34 (5.04)	2.19 (4.73)	2.13 (4.60)	3.22 (7.00)	2.93 (6.37)	2.81 (6.12)	3.15 (6.86)	3.17 (6.90)
9.	Other fallow lands	1.12 (2.41)	1.19 (2.58)	1.14 (2.46)	1.16 (2.51)	1.13 (2.46)	1.41 (3.07)	1.38 (3.01)	1.48 (3.22)	1.61 (3.52)
10.	Net area sown	29.93 (64.48)	30.38 (65.49)	30.60 (66.03)	31.03 (67.03)	30.09 (65.40)	30.03 (65.30)	30.23 (65.86)	29.91 (65.14)	29.84 (64.97)
11.	Area sown more than once	8.91 (19.19)	8.08 (17.41)	8.87 (19.14)	9.77 (21.11)	10.10 (21.95)	10.60 (23.05)	11.23 (24.47)	11.42 (24.87)	12.41 (27.02)
12.	Total cropped area	38.84 (83.67)	38.46 (82.90)	39.47 (85.17)	40.80 (88.14)	40.19 (87.35)	40.63 (88.35)	41.46 (90.33)	41.33 (90.01)	42.25 (91.99)
13.	Wasteland % of wasteland of reporting area	4.51 (9.72)	4.26 (9.18)	4.17 (9.00)	3.88 (8.38)	3.66 (7.95)	3.59 (7.81)	3.50 (7.63)	3.50 (7.62)	3.47 (7.55)

Note: Bracketed figures denote percentages to total reporting area.

Table 9.4 D : Land Utilization Statistics of Bundelkhand Region of UP. (in lakh hects.)

Sl. No.	*Land Use Category*	*1950-51*	*1955-56*	*1960-61*	*1965-66*	*1970-71*	*1971-72*	*1972-73*	*1973-74*	*1974-75*
1	*2*	*3*	*4*	*5*	*6*	*7*	*8*	*9*	*10*	*11*
1.	Reporting Area	29.79	30.67	30.06	30.04	29.95	NA	29.98	NA	29.09
2.	Forest	1.11	2.43	2.22	2.21	2.32	NA	2.33	NA	2.35
		(3.73)	(7.92)	(7.39)	(7.36)	(7.75)		(7.77)		(7.84)
3.	Barren and uncultiv-able waste	2.60	2.07	1.66	1.53	1.39	NA	1.43	NA	1.44
		(8.73)	(6.75)	(5.52)	(5.09)	(4.64)		(4.77)		(4.80)
4.	Land put to non-agri-cultural uses	1.46	1.48	1.53	1.53	1.54	NA	1.53	NA	1.54
		(4.90)	(4.83)	(5.09)	(5.09)	(5.14)		(5.10)		(5.14)
5.	Culturable waste	5.56	5.17	4.37	4.23	3.79	NA	3.77	NA	3.63
		(18.66)	(16.86)	(14.54)	(14.08)	(12.65)		(12.58)		(12.10)
6.	Permancnt pastures	NA	0.03	0.09	0.09	0.08	NA	0.08	NA	0.08
			(0.10)	(0.30)	(0.30)	(0.27)		0.27)		(0.27)
7.	Misc. trees and groves	0.78	0.55	0.46	0.41	0.33	NA	0.33	NA	0.33
		(2.62)	(1.79)	(1.53)	(1.36)	(1.10)		(1.10)		(1.10)
8.	Current fallow	2.16	0.00	0.00	1.25	1.12	NA	0.99	NA	1.45
		(7.25)			(4.16)	(3.74)		(3.30)		(4.83)
9.	Other fallow lands	1.31	2.65	2.45	1.34	1.03	NA	1.16	NA	1.10
		(4.40)	(8.64)	(8.15)	(4.46)	(3.44)		(3.87)		(3.67)
10.	Net area sown	14.81	16.28	17.27	17.42	18.36	NA	18.35	NA	18.07
		(49.71)	(53.08)	(57.45)	(57.99)	(61.30)		(61.21)		(60.25)
11.	Area sown more than once	0.94	1.09	1.58	1.43	1.89	NA	2.04	NA	1.68
		(3.16)	(3.55)	(5.26)	(4.76)	(6.31)		(6.80)		(5.60)
12.	Total cropped area	15.75	17.37	18.85	18.85	20.25	NA	20.39	NA	19.75
		(52.87)	(56.64)	(62.71)	(62.75)	(67.61)		(68.01)		(65.86)
13.	Wasteland % of wasteland to reporting area	8.16	7.27	6.12	5.85	5.26	NA	5.28	NA	5.15
		(27.39)	(23.71)	(20.36)	(19.47)	(17.56)		(17.62)		(17.17)

Table 9.4 D : (*Contd.*)

Sl. No.	*Land Use Category*	*1975-76*	*1976-77*	*1977-78*	*1978-79*	*1979-80*	*1980-81*	*1981-82*	*1982-83*	*1983-84*
1	*2*	*12*	*13*	*14*	*15*	*16*	*17*	*18*	*19*	*20*
1.	Reporting area	29.98	30.02	30.02	30.05	29.69	29.66	29.68	29.64	29.56
2.	Forest	2.35 (7.84)	2.51 (8.36)	2.48 (8.26)	2.49 (8.29)	2.41 (8.12)	2.40 (8.09)	2.41 (8.12)	2.41 (8.13)	2.41 (8.15)
3.	Barren and uncultivable waste	1.44 (4.80)	1.37 (4.56)	1.36 (4.53)	1.35 (4.49)	1.37 (4.61)	1.38 (4.65)	1.33 (4.48)	1.37 (4.62)	1.32 (4.47)
4.	Land put to non-agricultural uses	1.55 (5.17)	1.55 (5.16)	1.55 (5.16)	1.59 (5.29)	1.61 (5.42)	1.68 (5.66)	1.71 (5.76)	1.76 (5.94)	1.79 (6.06)
5.	Culturable waste	3.58 (11.94)	3.57 (11.89)	3.50 (11.66)	3.31 (11.01)	2.91 (9.80)	2.69 (9.07)	2.56 (8.63)	2.75 (9.28)	2.67 (9.03)
6.	Permanent pastures	0.08 (0.27)	0.09 (0.30)	0.09 (0.30)	0.09 (0.30)	0.10 (0.34)	0.10 (0.34)	0.10 (0.34)	0.10 (0.34)	0.09 (0.30)
7.	Misc. trees and groves	0.32 (1.07)	0.32 (1.07)	0.32 (1.07)	0.32 (1.06)	0.43 (1.45)	0.42 (1.42)	0.40 (1.35)	0.23 (0.78)	0.19 (0.64)
8.	Current fallow	1.33 (4.44)	1.32 (4.40)	1.29 (4.36)	1.28 (4.27)	1.63 (5.49)	1.49 (5.02)	1.40 (4.72)	1.37 (4.62)	1.36 (4.60)
9.	Other fallow lands	1.12 (3.74)	1.15 (3.83)	1.09 (3.63)	1.11 (3.69)	1.19 (4.01)	1.26 (4.25)	1.30 (4.38)	1.30 (4.39)	1.09 (3.69)
10.	Net area sown	18.21 (60.74)	18.14 (60.43)	18.34 (61.09)	18.51 (61.60)	18.04 (60.76)	18.24 (61.50)	18.47 (62.23)	18.35 (61.91)	18.64 (63.06)
11.	Area sown more than once	1.70 (5.67)	1.57 (5.23)	1.81 (6.03)	2.15 (7.15)	2.17 (7.31)	2.31 (7.79)	1.97 (6.64)	2.62 (8.84)	2.26 (7.65)
12.	Total cropped area	19.91 (66.41)	19.71 (65.66)	20.15 (67.12)	20.66 (68.75)	20.21 (68.07)	20.55 (69.29)	20.44 (68.87)	20.97 (70.75)	20.90 (70.71)
13.	Wasteland % of wasteland to reporting area	5.10 (17.01)	5.03 (16.45)	4.95 (16.49)	4.75 (15.80)	4.38 (14.75)	4.17 (14.06)	3.99 (13.45)	4.22 (14.24)	4.08 (13.80)

Note : Bracketed figures denote percentages to total reporting area.

Table 9.4 E : Land Utilization Statistics of Hill Region of U.P. (in lakh hects.)

Sl. No.	Land Use Category	1950-51	1955-56	1960-61	1965-66	1970-71	1971-72	1972-73	1973-74	1974-75
1	2	3	4	5	6	7	8	9	10	11
1.	Reporting area	49.59	50.20	48.74	49.31	51.65	NA	51.87	NA	51.92
2.	Forest	24.07 (48.54)	24.53 (48.86)	22.78 (46.74)	23.31 (47.27)	32.55 (63.02)	NA	32.99 (63.60)	NA	34.23 (65.93)
3.	Barren and uncultiv-able waste	14.03 (28.29)	14.02 (27.93)	14.56 (29.87)	14.55 (29.51)	4.26 (8.25)	NA	4.25 (8.18)	NA	2.31 (4.45)
4.	Land put to non-agri-cultural uses	0.33 (0.67)	0.37 (0.74)	0.36 (0.74)	0.39 (0.79)	0.41 (0.79)	NA	0.39 (0.75)	NA	1.05 (2.02)
5.	Culturable waste	0.89 (1.79)	0.36 (0.72)	0.29 (0.59)	0.25 (0.51)	0.19 (0.37)	NA	0.18 (0.35)	NA	2.92 (5.62)
6.	Permanent pastures	NA	0.08 (0.16)	0.02 (0.04)	0.00	0.00	NA	0.00	NA	1.97 (3.79)
7.	Misc. trees and groves	2.25 (4.54)	2.09 (4.16)	1.85 (3.80)	1.83 (3.71)	6.56 (12.70)	NA	6.44 (12.42)	NA	1.96 (3.77)
8.	Current fallow	0.48 (0.97)	0.31 (0.62)	0.32 (0.66)	0.39 (0.79)	0.31 (0.60)	NA	0.21 (0.40)	NA	0.22 (0.42)
9.	Other fallow lands	0.08 (0.16)	0.28 (0.56)	0.19 (0.39)	0.03 (0.06)	0.08 (0.15)	NA	0.03 (0.06)	NA	0.32 (0.62)
10.	Net area sown	7.45 (15.02)	8.17 (16.27)	8.36 (17.15)	8.56 (17.36)	7.32 (14.17)	NA	7.17 (13.82)	NA	6.94 (13.37)
11.	Area sown more than once	1.26 (2.54)	1.49 (2.97)	1.67 (3.43)	1.86 (3.77)	4.81 (9.31)	NA	5.35 (10.31)	NA	3.97 (7.65)
12.	Total cropped area	8.72 (17.58)	9.67 (5.32)	10.03 (20.58)	10.42 (21.13)	12.13 (23.48)	NA	12.52 (24.14)	NA	10.91 (21.01)
13.	Wasteland % of wasteland to reporting area	14.92 (30.06)	14.46 (28.81)	14.87 (30.50)	14.80 (30.02)	4.45 (8.62)	NA	4.43 (8.54)	NA	7.20 (13.86)

Table 9.4 E: (*Contd.*)

Sl. No.	*Land Use Category*	*1975-76*	*1976-77*	*1977-78*	*1978-79*	*1979-80*	*1980-81*	*1981-82*	*1982-83*	*1983-84*
1	*2*	*12*	*13*	*14*	*15*	*16*	*17*	*18*	*19*	*20*
1.	Reporting area	51.81	51.44	51.75	52.81	53.23	53.27	53.08	53.22	53.35
2.	Forest	34.33	33.54	34.05	34.04	34.37	34.43	34.40	34.40	34.38
		(66.26)	(65.20)	(65.80)	(64.46)	(64.57)	(64.63)	(64.81)	(64.64)	(64.44)
3.	Barren and uncultivable waste	2.31	2.31	2.31	2.89	2.89	2.90	2.90	2.90	2.89
		(4.46)	(4.49)	(4.46)	(5.47)	(5.43)	(5.44)	(5.46)	(5.45)	(5.42)
4.	Land put to non-agricultural uses	1.05	1.06	1.06	1.20	1.19	1.18	1.18	1.18	1.19
		(2.03)	(2.06)	(2.05)	(2.27)	(2.24)	(2.22)	(2.22)	(2.22)	(2.23)
5.	Culturable waste	2.92	2.88	2.88	3.16	3.16	3.16	3.16	3.16	3.16
		(5.64)	(5.60)	(5.57)	(5.98)	(5.94)	(5.93)	(5.95)	(5.94)	(5.92)
6.	Permanent pastures	1.98	1.98	1.98	2.17	2.17	2.17	2.17	2.17	2.17
		(3.82)	(3.85)	(3.83)	(4.11)	(4.08)	(4.07)	(4.09)	(4.00)	(4.07)
7.	Misc. trees and groves	1.96	1.96	1.96	1.87	1.86	1.86	1.85	1.85	1.85
		(3.78)	(3.81)	(3.79)	(354)	(3.49)	(3.49)	(3.49)	(3.48)	(3.47)
8.	Current fallow	0.26	0.24	0.23	0.19	0.21	0.21	0.21	0.20	0.20
		(0.50)	(0.47)	(0.44)	(0.36)	(0.39)	(0.39)	(0.40)	(0.38)	(0.37)
9.	Other fallow lands	0.29	0.29	0.29	0.31	0.31	0.32	0.32	0.33	0.33
		(0.56)	(0.56)	(0.56)	(0.59)	(0.58)	(0.61)	(0.60)	(0.62)	(0.62)
10.	Net area sown	6.71	7.18	6.99	6.98	7.07	7.04	6.89	7.03	7.18
		(12.95)	(13.96)	(13.51)	(13.22)	(13.28)	(13.22)	(12.98)	(13.21)	(13.46)
11.	Area sown more than once	4.15	4.09	4.17	4.19	4.31	4.44	4.37	4.42	4.33
		(8.01)	(7.95)	(8.06)	(7.93)	(8.10)	(8.33)	(8.23)	(8.31)	(8.12)
12.	Total cropped area	10.86	11.27	11.16	11.17	11.38	11.48	11.26	11.45	11.51
		(20.96)	(21.91)	(21.57)	(21.15)	(21.38)	(21.55)	(21.21)	(2.52)	(21.58)
13.	Wasteland % of wasteland to reporting area	7.21	7.17	7.17	8.22	8.22	8.23	8.23	8.23	8.22
		(13.92)	(13.94)	(13.86)	(15.56)	(15.45)	(15.44)	(15.50)	(15.47)	(15.41)

Note: Bracketed figures denote percentages to total reporting area.

Table 9.5A : Growth of land utilisation pattern (U.P.)

(Percentage)

Sl. No.	*Land Use Categories*	*During*					
		1960-61 over 1950-51	*1970-71 over 1960-61*	*1980-81 over 1970-71*	*1975-76 over 1965-66*	*1983-84 over 1975-76*	*1983-84 over 1980-81*
1	*2*	*3*	*4*	*5*	*6*	*7*	*8*
1.	Reporting area	0.08	0.11	-0.02	0.16	-0.04	+0.02
2.	Forest	1.74	2.70	+0.37	3.13	-1.03	-0.05
3.	Barren and uncultivable wasteland	-1.08	-5.85	-2.14	-7.02	-1.15	-1.03
4.	Land put to non-agricultural uses	-0.31	0.62	+1.15	0.85	+1.05	+1.03
5.	Culturable waste	-3.37	-1.96	-1.57	0.03	-3.43	-0.55
6.	Permanent pastures	NA	5.76	+14.38	15.51	+ 0.83	+0.34
7.	Misc. trees and groves	-4.50	3.50	-6.56	-0.25	-4.46	-4.93
8.	Current fallows	-16.67	17.46	+3.01	-0.74	+2.36	-0.31
9.	Other fallow land	15.78	-8.05	+2.77	0.99	+3.11	+2.59
10.	Net area sown	0.57	0.07	-0.05	-0.08	+0.05	+0.10
11.	Area sown more than once	2.00	2.65	+ 2.22	2.23	+3.55	+0.96
12.	Total cropped area	0.85	0.67	+ 0.57	0.45	+1.03	+0.66
13.	Wasteland	-1.94	-4.01	-0.94	-3.05	-2.03	-0.66

Table 9.5 B : Growth of land utilization pattern in Eastern Region of U.P.

(Percentage)

Sl. No.	*Land Use Categories*	*During*					
		1960-61 over 1950-51	*1970-71 over 1960-61*	*1975-76 over 1965-66*	*1980-81 over 1970-71*	*1983-84 over 1975-76*	*1983-84 over 1980-81*
1.	Reporting area	0.12	0.15	0.32	-0.11	-0.16	0.10
2.	Forest	5.62	2.38	4.00	-0.29	-0.45	-0.04
3.	Barren and uncultivable waste	-2.46	-1.05	-0.10	-1.96	-3.32	-1.14
4.	Land put to non-agri-cultural uses	0.25	0.21	0.44	1.10	1.56	1.60
5.	Culturable waste	-3.23	-2.03	2.08	-5.12	-5.73	-1.45
6.	Permanent pasture	NA	1.54	6.56	1.96	1.40	3.78
7.	Misc. trees and groves	-4.63	-0.58	0.28	-2.42	-4.90	-4.87
8.	Current fallows	-23.82	26.45	0.37	5.98	7.10	1.04
9.	Other fallow land	17.42	7.20	0.61	1.34	3.61	6.55
10.	Net area sown	0.44	0.15	0.04	-0.16	-0.28	-0.15
11.	Area sown more than once	1.13	0.86	0.49	2.71	4.06	1.61
12.	Total cropped area	0.60	0.32	0.14	0.64	0.95	0.40
13.	Wasteland	-2.79	-1.57	-1.10	-3.53	-4.39	-1.11

Table 9.5 C : Growth of land utilization pattern in Western Region of U.P.

(Percentage)

Sl. No.	*Land Use Categories*	*During*					
		1960-61 over 1950-51	*1970-71 over 1960-61*	*1975-76 over 1965-66*	*1980-81 over 1970-71*	*1983-84 over 1975-76*	*1983-84 over 1980-81*
1.	Reporting area	0.14	-0.10	-0.10	-0.46	-0.06	0.0
2.	Forest	9.26	-0.70	-0.46	0.32	0.0	0.0
3.	Barren and uncultivable waste	-2.08	-1.50	-1.38	-1.65	-2.05	-1.73
4.	Land put to non-agricultural uses	0.60	1.38	-0.85	0.74	0.67	0.59
5.	Culturable waste	-4.30	-2.10	-2.26	-5.44	-5.14	-0.19
6.	Permanent pasture	NA	12.07	1.68	-0.41	-1.00	0.0
7.	Misc. trees and groves	-6.15	-2.16	0.51	-6.46	-9.66	-5.79
8.	Current fallows	-10.93	11.90	-0.26	0.34	-1.63	-3.86
9.	Other fallow land	22.85	-9.00	2.55	4.25	3.68	0.85
10.	Net area sown	0.35	-0.03	0.30	0.10	0.25	0.23
11.	Area sown more than once	2.43	3.83	3.90	2.65	3.33	1.63
12.	Total cropped area	0.76	0.93	0.96	0.88	1.22	0.71
13.	Wasteland	-3.15	-1.53	-1.67	-0.17	-3.26	-1.08

Table 9.5 D : Growth of land utilization pattern in Central Region of U.P.

(Percentage)

Sl. No.	Land Use Categories	During					
		1960-61 over 1950-51	*1970-71 over 1960-61*	*1975-76 over 1965-66*	*1980-81 over 1970-71*	*1983-84 over 1975-76*	*1983-84 over 1980-81*
1.	Reporting area	0.14	-0.02	-0.07	-0.11	-0.13	-0.04
2.	Forest	6.22	1.00	-0.37	-0.46	-0.05	-0.14
3.	Barren and unculturable waste	-2.50	-1.16	-0.78	-1.78	-2.11	-1.11
4.	Land put to non-agri-cultural uses	-0.05	0.34	0.38	0.42	0.34	0.45
5.	Culturable waste	-2.60	-2.23	-1.84	-4.45	-4.83	-1.59
6.	Permanent pasture	NA	9.60	1.06	-1.05	-0.86	1.22
7.	Misc. trees and groves	-4.55	-2.63	-1.49	-2.70	-5.36	-6.74
8.	Current fallow	-17.42	22.83	3.34	3.34	2.66	2.66
9.	Other fallow lands	25.03	-7.95	0.85	2.51	4.64	4.52
10.	Net area sown	0.60	0.11	-0.12	-0.02	-0.04	-0.21
11.	Area sown more than once	2.43	1.37	0.38	1.42	4.23	5.40
12.	Total cropped area	0.97	0.39	-0.01	0.33	1.06	1.31
13.	Wasteland	-2.34	-1.32	-1.18	-2.98	-3.22	-1.13

Table 9.5 E : Growth of land utilization pattern in Bundelkhand Region of U.P.

(Percentage)

Sl. No.	*Land Use Categories*	*During*					
		1960-61 over 1950-51	*1970-71 over 1960-61*	*1975-76 over 1965-66*	*1980-81 over 1970-71*	*1983-84 over 1975-76*	*1983-84 over 1980-81*
1.	Reporting area	0.08	-0.04	0.02	-0.10	-0.18	-0.11
2.	Forest	7.17	0.44	0.62	0.34	0.32	0.14
3.	Barren and uncultivable waste	-4.40	-1.76	-0.06	-0.07	-1.08	-1.47
4.	Land put to non-agricultural uses	0.47	0.08	0.13	0.87	1.82	2.14
5.	Culturable waste	-2.38	-1.41	-1.67	-3.37	-3.60	-0.25
6.	Permanent pastures	NA	-1.15	-1.17	2.26	1.48	-3.45
7.	Misc. trees and groves	-5.14	-3.26	-2.46	2.44	-6.31	-23.23
8.	Current fallows	2.16	1.15	0.62	2.90	0.28	-3.00
9.	Other fallow land	6.46	-8.30	-1.78	2.04	-0.34	-4.72
10.	Net area sown	1.55	0.62	0.45	-0.07	0.29	0.73
11.	Area sown more than once	5.33	1.80	1.75	2.03	3.62	-0.73
12.	Total cropped area	1.81	0.72	0.55	0.15	0.61	0.56
13.	Wasteland	-2.84	-1.50	-1.36	-2.30	-2.75	-0.72

Table 9.5 F : Growth of land utilization pattern in Hill Region of U.P.

(Percentage)

Sl. No.	*Land Use Categories*	*During*					
		1960-61 over 1950-51	*1970-71 over 1960-61*	*1975-76 over 1965-66*	*1980-81 over 1970-71*	*1983-84 over 1975-76*	*1983-84 over 1980-81*
1.	Reporting area	0.18	0.58	0.50	0.31	0.37	0.05
2.	Forest	-0.56	3.63	3.95	0.56	0.02	-0.05
3.	Barren and uncultivable waste	0.37	-11.56	-16.80	-3.77	2.84	-0.12
4.	Land put to non-agri-cultural uses	0.87	1.30	10.41	11.15	1.58	0.28
5.	Culturable waste	-10.60	-4.14	27.86	32.46	1.00	0.0
6.	Permanent pastures	NA	0.0	7.06	1.40	1.15	0.0
7.	Misc. trees and groves	-1.94	13.50	0.70	-11.84	-0.72	-0.18
8.	Current fallow	-3.98	-0.32	-3.97	-3.82	-3.23	-1.61
9.	Other fallow lands	9.04	8.30	25.46	14.87	1.63	1.03
10.	Net area sown	1.16	-1.32	2.40	-0.39	0.85	0.66
11.	Area sown more than once	2.86	11.15	8.35	-0.80	0.53	-0.83
12.	Total cropped area	1.41	1.92	0.42	-0.55	0.73	0.09
13.	Wasteland	-0.03	-11.37	-6.94	6.34	1.65	-0.04

10

Wastelands of Rajasthan : A Peep into Changes, 1960-61 to 1984-85

N. L. Gupta and (Mrs.) S. Kothari

Physical and cultural diversity often gives rise to a complex variety of land uses, particularly in areas of historic evolution like Rajasthan. Population pressure and galloping human demands everywhere further complicate the process, patterns and trends of changes in the old established land utilization including wastelands in multiple ways.

Like India, the State of Rajasthan also has more than one-third of its total area under a variety of wastelands. Caused due to improper or non-optimum land use, such wastelands need to be looked upon as a potential resource. Resource-starved Rajasthan State at this juncture can ill-afford more than 8.58 million hectares of its land lying waste. Everywhere wastelands are being constantly reclaimed by various methods and under habitation, cultivation, afforestation and recreational planning.

Wastelands Defined

In definition, nomenclature and stock estimations, wastelands continue to defy desired scientific accuracy and unanimity of opinion. Earlier studies undertaken by the Ministry of Food and Agriculture (1961), Planning Commission, Government of India (1963 and 1965), Ministry of Home Affairs (1972), etc., also attempted in this direction. However, their greater relevance and focus so far has been with the cultivation activities, problems and potentialities, Stamp (1948), Shafi, M.(1968), Singh (Mrs.) A.L. (1977), Vohra, (1980), Jain, A. (1983), Goojar, K.S. (1985), etc.

However, the Wasteland Survey and Reclamation Committee (1961) defined wastelands as those lands which are either not available for cultivation or are left out as fallows and cultivable wastes and thus embrace the following types:

(a) Land not available for cultivation—barren and uncultivated land.
(b) Other uncultivated lands excluding fallows—culturable waste, permanent pasture and grazing lands, and land under miscellaneous tree crops and groves.
(c) Fallows—current as well as of other types.

Wastelands include barren lands degraded to varying degrees through wind and water erosion, through deforestation, overgrazing, etc. Such lands are also waterlogged, saline and alkaline, "usar" and kans-infested, rocky outcrops, stony and pebbly hill slopes, sand-arid wastes. Often their reclamation with existing knowledge and under present circumstances proves prohibitive to rural masses. In the present study the wastelands of Rajasthan have been investigated on the basis of the following categories:

(1) Non-cultivable Wasteland
    (a) Barren and uncultivable land
(2) Cultivable Wasteland
    (a) Old fallows, (b) culturable wastes.

The Study Area

Rajasthan, after Madhya Pradesh, is the second largest State of the Indian Union with 3,42,239 sq.km area (i.e. nearly 10.43% of India), is situated in its drier western part between 23°4' 10" and 30°15' 5" north latitudes and 69°30' 5" and 78°16' 50" east longitudes and is roughly quadrilateral in shape. Administratively, it has 27 districts and 205 tehsils. One of the oldest and deeply rugged and dissected Aravalli mountains, averaging 600 to 700 metres high above m.s.l. extend diagonally across it in south-west to north-east direction, and towards east and west of these hills lie the vast and varied plains, semi-arid to arid in character.

Chambal and Mahi as perennial rivers in south-east and south along with their numerous drier tributaries provide the drainage to most of eastern Rajasthan which stands in utter contrast to its counterpart drier Luni and its numerous ephemeral tributaries and few inland basins towards west. In north, dry Ghaggar bed often floods parts of Sri Ganganagar district during the monsoons.

Climatically, Rajasthan is largely arid in the west, sub-arid in the centre and sub-humid in the east and south-east. Thus, a wide range of temperatures with occasional extremes, low monsoonal rainfall and relative humidity characterize its climatic conditions. This hottest region of India experiences blinding sandy duststorms along with high velocity winds in summers and paucity of rains in its west, but, protected by Aravalli ranges towards east, has different and distinguishing characteristics. The mean annual rainfall varies from 21 cm at Jaisalmer in the west to about 85 cm in Banswara and Hadoti areas in the south and south-east, i.e. decreasing in east to west direction. Such a situation accounts for frequent droughts and famines in the State and more so towards its western margins. In innumerable ways, wastelands of Rajasthan depict close relationships with these geographically varied micro-climatic conditions.

According to 1981 Census, 34.26 million population of Rajasthan constituted about 5.13 per cent of India's total population and 100 persons per km^2 density (compared with 216 for India) indicated thin distribution. Whereas 21 per cent of its people lived in 201 towns and cities, the remaining 79 per cent belonged to the rural sector, distributed in 37,124 villages. During 1971-1981 decade, it recorded the highest growth rate in India, *viz.* 32.97 per cent, whereas its overall literacy percentage of 24.38 per cent (36.2% in India) was low and 17.73 per cent for rural areas was significantly lower. The share of the Scheduled Castes, Scheduled Tribes and non-scheduled persons in the total population of the State was recorded as 17.04, 12.21 and 70.75 per cent respectively. All these demographic factors had their inescapable bearing on the trends and changes in wastelands of the State.

Land Utilization Patterns and Trend, 1960-61 to 1984-85

Every region is characterized by a typical complex web of land utilization pattern, evolved and nurtured by people's history, art and culture on the one hand and determined and directed by its physical layout and resource base on the other influencing in its wake inevitably all futuristic policy decisions, programmes and developmental planning.

Rajasthan State has a greater share of area not available for cultivation (12.76%), other uncultivated land (25.15%) and fallow (11.68%) which finally contribute towards its wastelands in comparison to all its neighbouring States, and even India (1978-79). On the whole while the net sown area and forest lands showed a growth of 14.71 and 165.97 per cent during this period, i.e. a rise from 38.74 and 2.41 per cent in 1960-61 to 44.43 and 6.40 per cent in 1984-85 and their projection rise to 49.69 and 10.18 per cent respectively by A.D. 2000, land under all other categories indicated declines.

Growth and Trend of Wastelands

Table 10.1 indicates the overall decline in the total and individual category-wise wastelands in Rajasthan during 1960-61 to 1984-85 period from 44.61 to 31.96 per cent indicating 28.36 per cent growth rate and 21.17 per cent projection for A.D. 2001. In comparision, India's total wasteland during these 25 years also decreased from 22.28 to 13.8 per cent. Among the individual categories, however, the maximum decline has been recorded by "Barren and Uncultivable" lands in the State.

The average for Rajasthan State as a whole during this period in barren and uncultivable, culturable waste and old fallows has been 11.58, 18.84 and 6.89 per cent and an annual declining growth rate of 1.61, 0.34 and 0.53 per cent respectively.

Details of individual category-wise wastelands in districts in 1960- 61 and 1984-85 along with change have been indicated in Tables 10.3, 10.4 and 10.5. Barren and uncultivable lands indicate change in 38.89 per

Table 10.1: Rajasthan: Pattern of Wastelands, 1960-61 to 1984-85

(Figure in percentage)

Wasteland categories	*Years*						*Growth of % 1984-85 over 1960-61*	*Projection A.D. 2001*
	1960-61	*1965-66*	*1970-71*	*1975-76*	*1980-81*	*1984-85*		
Barren and Unculturable land	15.23	14.36	13.83	9.16	8.52	8.37	-45.04	1.09
Culturable Waste	20.21	19.03	17.92	19.44	18.75	17.68	-12.52	16.62
Old fallow	9.17	6.73	6.82	6.59	6.10	5.91	-35.55	3.46
Sate total	44.61	40.12	38.57	35.19	33.37	31.96	-28.36	21.17
State's share in India	—	—	—	—	—	—	—	—
India	22.28	N.A.	18.00	16.10	15.30	13.80	-38.06	7.25

Table 10.2: Rajasthan: District-wise changes in types of wastelands in 1984-85 over 1960-61

Barren and Uncultivable Land				*Culturable Waste*				*Old Fallows*			
Categories in %	*No. of districts in 1960-61*	*No. of districts in 1984-85*	*Change in 1984-85 over 1960-61*	*Categories in %*	*No. of districts in 1960-61*	*No. of districts in 1984-85*	*Change in 1984-85 over 1960-61*	*Categories in %*	*No. of districts in 1960-61*	*No. of districts in 1984-85*	*Change in 1984-85 over 1960-61*
<8.5	9	14	+5	<15.3	17	23	+6	<4.9	13	16	+3
8.5-17.0	4	10	+ 6	15.3-30.6	5	2	-3	4.9-9.8	6	9	+ 3
17.0-25.5	7	3	-4	30.6-45.9	3	1	-2	9.8-14.7	3	1	-2
25.5-34.0	3	–	-3	45.9-61.2	–	–	–	14.7-19.6	2	1	-1
34.0-42.5	3	–	-3	61.2-76.5	1	1	–	19.6-24.5	2	–	-2
Total	26	27	+11 -10	Total	26	27	+ 6 -5	Total	26	27	+ 6 -5

cent districts (Table 10.2), i.e. from 15.23 per cent in 1960 61 to 8.37 per cent in 1984-85 showing a decreasing per cent growth rate of 45.04. The decrease in the number of districts in high category and *vice versa* needs no emphasis.

In Table 10.2, culturable wasteland change in 19.81 per cent districts, i.e. from 20.21 per cent in 1960-61 to 17.68 per cent in 1984-85 indicating a declining growth rate of 12.52 per cent also reflects the diminishing number of districts in the higher category classes and *vice versa*. Table 10.2 on old fallow wastes also indicates similar changes and trend in 19.52 per cent districts, i.e. from 9.17 per cent in 1960-61 to 5.91 per cent in 1984-85 but a bit higher decreasing growth rate of 35.55 per cent.

Fig. 10.1 reveals individual district-wise growth and trends in total wasteland in Rajasthan over 25 years indicating wide fluctuations. While Jaisalmer and Bikaner districts in the west record maximum of wastelands, followed by districts of southern Rajasthan in 1960-61 and 1984-85 (Table 10.3), in contrast districts in mid-north-east register its minimum. Except Jhunjhunu, all other districts throughout Rajasthan indicate wasteland decrease in 1984-85 over 1960-61.

Wasteland projections by A.D. 2001 indicate minus figures for the two districts of Sri Ganganagar and Churu and Jaisalmer still continue to lead all districts with the highest percentage under it. The state as a whole will still carry wasteland average of 21.17 per cent and seven districts above average percentage while the remaining eight will still range between 10 and 20 per cent and the rest below 10 per cent.

Geographically, the spatial distributional pattern of wastelands reveals its actual location, siting and even block sizes, adding thereby its applied relevance to such a survey and evaluation.

This spatial distribution of wastelands in Rajasthan indicates dominance of sand dunes and sandy wastes all-over its western and northern portions, the gullied and ravinous lands in the south-eastern part but the omnipresent hilly wastes caused by indiscriminate deforestation appear in mere patches of undulating uplands with or without scrub. Barren hill ridge and rock outcrop shown in scattered patches should in fact cover wide areas throughout the Aravallis.

District and Tehsil-wise Distribution of Wasteland

Both in Table 10.4 and Fig. 10.2-A-B district-wise distribution of

Table 10.3 : Rajasthan: District-wise growth of wasteland: 1960- 61 and 1984-85
(Figures in percentage)

Districts	*Growth in % 1984-85 over 1960-61*	*Projection A.D. 2001*	*Districts*	*Growth in % 1984-85 over 1960-61*	*Projection A.D. 2001*
1. Ajmer	-27.37	24.50	15. Jaisalmer	-4.21	57.21
2. Alwar	-25.94	14.96	16. Jalore	-16.21	19.51
3. Banswara	-47.66	8.15	17. Jhalawar	-54.41	11.16
4. Barmer	-25.89	22.62	18. Jhunjhunu	+ 12.66	9.01
5. Bharatpur	-62.61	5.08	19. Jodhpur	-15.48	24.54
6. Bhilwara	-58.20	22.81	20. Kota	-57.01	2.06
7. Bikaner	-30.45	39.37	21. Nagaur	-37.42	5.52
8. Bundi	-45.13	6.19	22. Pali	-24.59	20.16
9. Chittorgarh	-35.23	13.66	23. S. Madhopur	-57.14	3.32
10. Churu	-61.05	-2.33	24. Sikar	-6.00	13.68
11. Dholpur	–	–	25. Sirohi	-39.71	11.06
12. Dungarpur	-16.63	18.82	26. Tonk	-48.11	4.87
13. Sri Ganga-nagar	-66.21	-6.41	27. Udaipur	28.15	26.62
14. Jaipur	-34.64	-8.53			
- *Total Rajasthan*				-28.36	21.17

wastelands for 1960-61 and 1984-85 has been indicated category-wise along with change (Fig. 10.2-C). Both reveal that the number of districts and their respective percentage in the four out of five higher categories record a decrease in 1984-85 over 1960-61 (thus decrease being more marked in the two categories of 40.4 to 57.4 and 23.4 to 40.4), whereas in the last and lowest category in which the number of distracts has gone up from 4 to 14 indicating 36.47 per cent growth.

Fig. 10.2-A, B vividly show district-wise changes in wastelands in Rajasthan over this period. Whereas Jaisalmer district maintains its position in VH category with 91.17 per cent and 87.33 per cent wastelands in 1960-61 and 1984-85 respectively (i.e. a decrease of only 4.21%, Fig. 10.2-C) dominated by sand dunes and rocky wastes and most of the northern and eastern districts have shifted from L to VL category, i.e. 23.4-40.4 to 6.4-23.4 (Jhunjhunu with lowest percentage of wasteland in Rajasthan recorded a slight increase from 6.4 to 7.21%), districts of central and southern Rajasthan have registered a similar decline from M to L and Bhilwara in particular, from H to M category, *viz.* from 72.92 to 42.44 per cent, indicating 58.20 per cent growth on the minus side.

Table 10.4 : Rajasthan : District-wise change in wasteland: from 1960-61 to 1984-85

Categories in %	*1960-61 Districts*		*1984-85 Districts*		*Change in 1984-85 over 1960-61 in districts*	
	No.	*% to total*	*No.*	*% to total*	*No.*	*% to total*
6.4-23.4	4	15.38	14	51.85	+ 10	+ 36.57
23.4-40.4	13	50.00	10	37.04	-3	-12.96
40.4-57.4	6	23.08	2	7.41	- 4	-15.67
57.4-74.4	1	3.85	–	0.00	-1	-3.85
74.4-91.4	2	7.69	1	3.70	-1	-3.99
Total	26	100.00	27	100.00	+10 -9	+ 36.47 -36.47

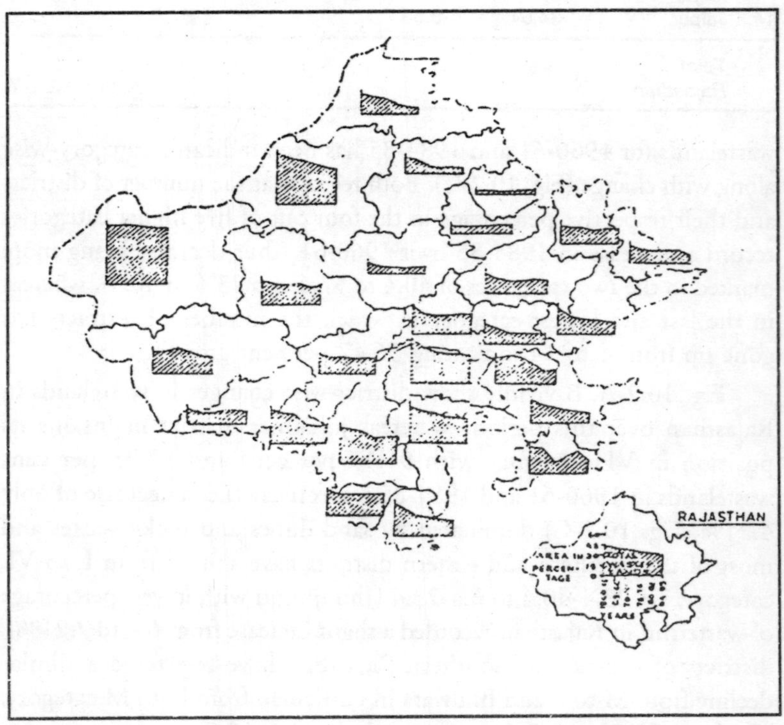

Fig. 10.1 : Rajasthan, District-wise trend in wastelands—1960-61 to 1984-85.

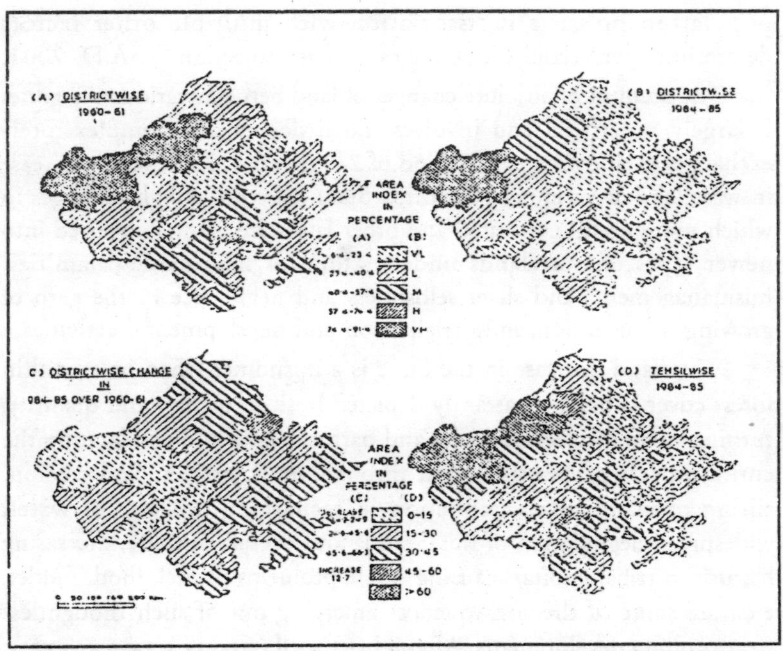

Fig. 10.2 : Rajasthan, wasteland distribution—1960-61 to 1984-85.

In terms of micro-level tehsil-wise distribution for 1984-85 (Fig. 10.2-D), a more precise and reliable picture emerges. Four broadly generalized wasteland regions emerge, *viz.* (1) Jaisalmer-Bikaner region wherein tehsil-wise wasteland ranges between 30 and above 60 per cent. (2) North-eastern region with 0 to 15 per cent wastelands lying mostly in Sri Ganganagar, Churu, Nagaur, Jhunjhunu and Sikar districts and scattered patches in Alwar, Bharatpur and Kota districts (encompassing 60 tehsils in all); (3) Central and southern Aravalli region with 30 to 60 per cent wasteland lying mostly in Ajmer, Bhilwara, Chittorgarh and Udaipur districts dominated by barren and rocky hilly wastes; and (4) Widely spread category of 15 to 30 per cent wasteland (covering as many as 90 tehsils out of 205 in the State) in south-western and eastern parts and scattered patches all-over the State.

Conclusion

The foregoing analysis supported by micro-specific details explains population pressure in association with multiple other factors determining wasteland variations as well as projection for A.D. 2001.

The account of absolute changes of land between various categories is largely superficial and involves much deeper and complex inter-exchanges even over a brief period of 2-3 decades. The overall decrease in wasteland at various levels in the State fails to highlight changes in which more useful cultivated and other lands are being converted into newer types of wastelands under natural or man-made calamities, mismanagements and sheer selfishness and negligence in the garb of growing urbanization, industrialization and developmental activities.

Wasteland decrease in the State is a misnomer when its ever thin forest cover is being constantly depleted both in quality and quantity, turning them into severe rocky and barren wastes and accelerating the entire process of desertification throughout Rajasthan. Soil erosion, silting of waterbodies, reduction in recharging capacity of water, widespread degradation of flora;-fauna and overall wild-life, increasing hazards in tribal habitats causing severe problems of fuel, food, fodder, etc., are some of the consequences emerging out of such thoughtless steam-rolling developments. After a brief spell of rainy season greenery, not only pastures and grazing lands of the State either dryout or are overgrazed but turn into virtual wastelands. Unfortunately, such forest and pasture grazing lands, in record and by occupation rights, do not fall into the wasteland category which otherwise belong to it in a large measure.

Reclamation of wasteland is a slow and tedious process and though, in economic terms, less viable in its earlier stages, people have taken to it depending on contiguity and accessibility of such lands, their resource input capability and under the ever-growing pressure of population. Such efforts in end provide lower agricultural productivity as compared to other favourable areas of our country and yet people are compelled to undertake it in the absence of other alternative economic activities. The above process naturally involves higher cost at all levels and in all respects and, therefore, in terms of long-term planned developmental process, requires judicious policy decisions, selection of places and people for reclamation programmes, ultimately leading towards desired ecological equilibrium in any region.

Looking to the enormity and graveness of wasteland reclamation urgency, including the programme of reforesting 5 million hectares of barren and wasteland annually, the strategy and approach should be (1) to take its scale and rate into consideration, (2) genuine involvement of rural masses and non-governmental organizations even at village level, (3) smooth transfer of ownership and benefits of such lands to people who grow trees, grasses, fodder, etc., on it and not to those who only manage to own these, (4) make it really a massive nationwide development programme, cornering the avoidable controversy of development environment and instead encouraging "development without destruction" concept, and (5) to, educate and motivate, communicate and interact, develop self-confidence and grow greater awareness for the programme along with all access to finances and resources, available technologies, training and demonstration among concerned masses, tiding over the known administrative hurdles and gearing it to rise to the occasion.

REFERENCES

Gupta, N.L. (1965). *Land Utilization in Udaipur Plateau*. Unpublished Ph.D.Thesis, Udaipur University.

Gupta, N.L., & Kothari, S. (1986). *Wastelands of Southern Rajasthan Issues, Problems and Potentialities, 1966-61 to 1984-85*. Paper presented at 8th NAGI Congress, Srinagar.

Gupta, N.L., & Kothari, S. (1986). *Wasteland in Udaipur District: A Geographical Analysts and Evaluation, 1959-60 to 1984-85*. Paper sent for publication in *Annal of NAGI*, Pune.

Gupta, N.L., & Kothari, S. (1986). *Other Uncultivated Lands: A Case Study of Salumber Tehsil, Udaipur District, Southern Rajasthan*. Paper sent for publication in *Geog. Rev of India*, Calcutta.

Jain, Anita (1983). *Wasteland Utilization in Udaipur District, Problems and Prospects*. Unpublished Ph.D. Thesis, Sukhadia University.

Madiman, S.G. (Ed) (1957). *Readings in Land Utilization*, Vol. V, Bombay.

Misra, V.C. (1967). *Geography of Rajasthan*, New Delhi, NBT.

Pandey, S. (1977). *Changing Pattern of Cultivable Waste in Pharendra Tehsil (U.P)*, U.H.Bh.Pal. XIII, 1 & 2.

Shafi, M. (1968). "The Problems of Wastelands in India," *The Geographer*, Special No. XXI, Vol. XV.

Singh Abha L. (Mrs) (1977). "The Distribution and Utilization of Uncultivated lands in Koil Tehsil", *Geog. Rev. of India*, XXXIX, 3.

Basic Statistics of Rajasthan, 1984.

"Mapping of Wastelands in India from Satellite Imagery, 1980-82", Summary Report, Rajasthan, *NRSA*, Hyderabad, 1985.

Ministry of Food and Agriculture; Government of India, (1961). Wasteland Survey and Reclamation Committee, Report on the Locational and Utilization of Wastelands is India, Part X, U.P., New Delhi.

Planning Commission Committee on National Researches Study on Wastelands including Saline Alkaline and Waterlogged Lands and their Reclamation Measures.

Statistical Abstracts, Rajasthan, Jaipur, 1980, 1981, 1982.

Statistics Department, Board of Revenue, Government of Rajasthan, Ajmer.

11

Land-Utilisation Mapping to Estimate the Wastelands of Arid Zone in Rajasthan by Photo-Interpretation Technique*

Amal Kumar Sen

Introduction

Estimation of wasteland is of great importance to evaluate the potentialities of land for agricultural planning. A clear picture of the present situation is obtained when the land utilisations and their extent are presented in the form of maps. In Rajasthan, where the resources have not been fully assessed yet and whatever resources are available are not being properly utilised, the need for this study has been strongly felt. At the same time, a necessity has also been felt to find out some quick methods of land-utilisation survey and mapping to frame an early resource utilisation planning. Photo-interpretation and photogrammetric methods, which are the recent additions to our knowledge of modern cartography, are being applied now in the Central Arid Zone Research Institute for this work, and it has been found that these not only expedite survey work but also increase the efficiency of mapping.

* Reprinted from the proceedings of Symposium on "Reclamation and use of wastelands in India", Indian National Science Academy, New Delhi, from May 10-12, 1968.

Land-Utilisation in Rajasthan

The arid zone of Rajasthan comprises a total area of 1,81,062 sq kms. Viewing geographical aspects and available information, five classes of land-utilisation units are identified and mapped (Sen and Gupta, 1968) in Rajasthan, illustrating present land use for 1963-64 and land use changes between the years 1957-58 to 1962-63. The data are collected from the statistical abstracts (1959-1965) published by the Directorate of Economics and Statistics of the Government of Rajasthan. The land utilisation units identified are:

1. Forests
2. Settlements and other non-agricultural lands. This includes settlements, roads, railways, public buildings, water features, mountains, rocky areas etc.
3. Land not available for cultivation including barren lands, rocky areas, extensive sandy tracts, permanent grasses, shifting dunes.
4. Fallow lands which include current fallow. These are available for cultivation.
5. Cultivated lands which can be further classified under single-cropped and double-cropped lands.

The third and the fourth categories represent the wastelands, which can be called unculturable and culturable wastelands respectively.

Analysis of Wastelands

A high concentration of unculturable waste is noticed in the extreme arid tracts of Jaisalmer district (44.60% of total area) due to the extensive sandy tracts, rocky barren lands and shifting sand dunes. In other parts of the arid zone, the percentage of uncluturable waste is low (often below 10%) because of the tendency to put maximum land under crop, however low the production may be. On the other hand, culturable wastelands are high in the districts under arid zone like Barmer (40.94%), Bikaner (77.80%), Jaisalmer (50.25%), Jodhpur (41.28 %),

Jalore (24.51%), Pali (28.97%) and Nagaur (26.30%). The difficulties of putting more land under permanent cropped land lie in the existence of extensive dune land, rocky land, saline patches and saline soils, low groundwater-table and absence of irrigational facilities.

Our study, however, indicates that still there is scope to put at least 25 per cent of more land in almost all the districts of the arid zone, under plough. At the same time figures of land use changes do not indicate any significant changes in the rise of cultivated lands or fall in the extent of wastelands. This necessitates a rethinking of the problem and it appears that a land-utilisation survey is to locate and delineate the land-utilisation units in maps for estimating the extent of waste and cultivated lands. This can help the better utilization of the wastelands.

Photo-interpretation to map the wastelands and other land-utilisation units

To expedite the survey and mapping work, photo-interpretation methods are now being applied in the Institute. Recently, some work has been undertaken with some photographs of Pali (1 : 25,000), Bikaner (1:30,000) and Jalore (1:40,000) area. The object of this pilot project is to work out suitable methods to classify and map the land-utilisation units through photo-interpretation techniques. These photographs are vertical having slight or no tilt and distortions of 2 per cent which is also negligible. The emulsion used is of the Panchromatic type. The photographs are so chosen to cover approximately 30 sq kms area in each case.

Experimental

The photographs are stereoscopically examined to analyse the images by systematically analysing the structure and texture of the images and their correlations. The first interpretation work is confined to the preparation of the charts of the effective areas of each photographs showing topographic sequences. Accordingly, the following "Key" for interpretation is established :

(i) Hills
(ii) Sloping hill sides
(iii) Water features
(iv) Settlement and associated orchards
(v) Dunes
(vi) Sandy land
(vii) River side or stream side sandy lands
(viii) Rocky lands
(ix) Lands having demarcation of indiviudal holdings (plot boundaries)—Appears to be cultivated land.

This direct analysis gives some indications of wastelands. It appears that Nos. (i), (ii), (v), (vi) and (viii) are the key form the wastelands. But the images of dunes in both Bikaner and Jalore area show sharp contracts, having dark tones with dots and white tones in places. Examination on the field indicate the former being the dunes which are cultivated and as such strictly cannot be included in the wasteland group. A second interpretation is then carried out to classify the images in detail and in relation to the shape, size, and approach of the images identified in *the photographs*. In Pali and Jalore areas, the following scheme was worked out:

(i) Hills—having 3 different image characteristics
(ii) Sloping hill sides having 3 different images
(iii) Dunes—having two different characteristics of images
(iv) Sandy lands having four different image charactristics
(v) River side sandy lands—no variation of images
(vi) Rocky land—no variation of images
(vii) Lands having demarcation of individual holdings—having 11 different images.

A stereo-photo map was then prepared for the whole area according to the variations of the images of the photographs. The key, thus obtained, through direct interpretation was examined on sample basis, along a transect in the filed for identifications in Pali area. The results obtained were:

Hill—Wasteland-unculturable, rocky
Sloping hill sides—Fallow land
Dunes (i) Cultivated
(ii) Fallow
Sandy lands— (i) Wasteland—unfit for cultivation
(ii) Wasteland—fit for cultivation
(iii) Cultivated
(iv) Current fallow.
River side sandy lands—Current fallow
Lands having demarcation of individual holdings—cultivated.

The variation of images is found to be due to different cropping patterns. The tonal variation of the images are required to be established by another interpretation. Accordingly along with the field checking, the key established by photo-interpretation enables one to prepare a broad land-utilisation map, which indicates the extent of wastelands as well. Thus, the identification and maping of land-utilisation through photo-interpretation technique is mostly an indirect one.

The work is now being continued to standardise the method to suit different areas. The study conducted, so far, indicates that the systematic photo-interpretation, particularly that of correlation of the texture and the structure of the images gives sufficient data to establish a key for land-utilisation mapping. This exercise can be conducted as a preliminary to the field study, particularly to check the stereo-photo map and this can restrict the field-work to the examination of samples selected through the key of photo-interpretation.

Conclusion

The adoption of photo-interpretation technique indicates the following :

(i) Use of aerial photographs can expedite land-utilisation survey.

(ii) It enables preparation of tentative land-use maps before the survey is undertaken in the field.

(iii) It minimises field-work as this may be confined to sample areas of the same units identified by photo-interpretation.

(iv) At least three interpretations are necessary to prepare the key for mapping.

(v) In the laboratroy stereo-photo maps can be prepared for an area of about 30 sq. miles within a fortnight. For subsequent field checking of the units identified about five days' work is adequate. Unaided by air photographs field traverses alone cannot furnish such details in such a short period.

REFERENCES

Anoymous (1959-65), *Statistical Abstracts*, Government of Rajasthan, Directorate of Economics and Statistics, Jaipur.,

Sen, A.K. and Gupta, K.N. (1968), "Land-use and land-use changes in Rajasthan". *Indian Geogr. J.*

12

Estimate of Wastelands in India*

D.R. Bhumbla and *Arvind Khare*

Section I : Introduction

The agro-climatic conditions in India vary from cold deserts at sub-zero temperatures with meagre vegetation to dense tropical forests with a precipitation around 2500 mm. The entire range of rainfall from less than 50 mm to above 250 mm is well represented in the sub-continent. While some of the problems afflicting those lands are inherent, some are the result of increasing human and cattle needs, centuries of unscientific agricultural practices and geological evolution. On the one hand, there are problems of soil erosion along hill slopes, landslides, stream bank erosion, and on the other, there are problems like shifting sand dunes and extreme moisture stress. The problem of sheet erosion cut across geographical locations and is widely prevalent in the Indo-Gangetic alluvium soils of northern India, black soils of western Madhya Pradesh, Maharashtra, Andhra Pradesh, Karnataka and eastern and southern red soils. Increasing pressure of human and animal needs, rapid denudation, biotic interference in natural regeneration have contributed to increasing surface flow of rainwater and severe top soil erosion leading to siltation of canals, reservoirs and tanks in all regions. The same holds good for the problem of salinity and alkalinity. While some problems like ravines are restrictively located, others like drainage problem are widely distributed across the country.

---

* Published by the Society for Promotion of Wastelands Development, New Delhi.

It will not be an exaggeration to state that the problem of deterioration in the productive capability of these lands is truly a national one cutting across geographic and political boundaries. An investigation into the causes of land degradation is absolutely necessary. However, it is beyond the scope of this chapter to make such an attempt. It is also pertinent to mention that although the capacity of nature to maintain ecological balance is enormous, "there is a critical limit, beyond which the rate of deterioration is too great to be checked by nature's own recuperative process, ... before the critical limit is reached and nature's process is helped by scientific methods of conservation, the original ecological balance may be partially regained."[1] The scientific efforts in this direction will be greatly helped if a proper identification and estimation of degraded lands can be made. This chapter attempts to make a first approximation in estimating the extent of wastelands in this country.

Section II : Definition

There is no well-accepted definition of wastelands. For some time a definition based on economic potential and actual returns from land seems to have found some acceptance. It says that any land which is giving less than twenty per cent of its economic potential is a wasteland, it is not very helpful. The reasons are as under :

> It is a dynamic definition based on productivity which itself is dependent on the state of technology and its usage. As the technology improves, the productive potential of land increases but actual increase in production will be a function of acceptance and utilisation of improved technology over a period of time. This definition, therefore, makes wastelands a function of state of technology, incidence of its acceptance and time. A change in any of these factors shall change the designation of a piece of land into wastelands and *vice versa*. A continuous improvement in technology will make it more difficult, if not improbable, to estimate the extent of wastelands on the basis of this definition.

> Another aspect of this definition, because of its heavy bias on economics, is the neglect of ecological considerations. Thus, if any land which is giving proper economic returns b,ut is an ecological hazard shall not be counted as wasteland. From a macro point of view this does not seem to be acceptable.

The concern in this chapter, therefore, is to develop a working definition of wastelands which will help in its quantitative estimate and at the same time shall not neglect ecological considerations. Keeping these factors in view, the definition used in this chapter is as under :

> "Those lands are wastelands which are (a) ecologically unstable, (b) whose top soil has been nearly completely lost, and (c) which have developed toxicity in the root zones for growth of most plants, both annual crops and trees."

This definition will cover all those lands which are affected by :

- water erosion
- wind erosion
- floods
- waterlogging
- soil salinisation
- soil alkalinisation

Section III : Earlier Estimates

In this section, some of the earlier estimates have been evaluated to determine their shortcomings and strengths which can help in developing a better methodology of estimation and Section II states the definition of wastelands.

The estimate made by the Ministry of Agriculture gives a figure of 175 million hectares.[2] The methodlogy adopted by them has two discrete steps:

- firstly they have assumed certain percentage of area under each category of land use (as determined by the Department of Economics and Statistics, Ministry of Agriculture) to be problem area.
- in the second step, area under specific problem category has been estimated and added to the area calculated in the first step to arrive at a figure of 175 million hectares.

The error in this estimate is obviously on the higher side. The areas under specific problem category has already been accounted for in the first step because irrespective of the problem afflicting a particular area, it had to fall in one of the land use categories and by taking a percentage of each land use category as problem area, all type of problem categories are covered in the first step. The addition of area under specific problem categories has therefore inflated the estimate by double counting some of the areas. Some other estimates also suffer from the error of overlapping of categories. In this chapter, attempt will be made to specifically avoid this error and whenever it is not possible to do so, at least quantify the range of error.

(a) Land use classification

The Directorate of Economics and Statistics of the Ministry of Agriculture provides the following classification of land use in India:

1. Forests
2. Area put to non-agricultural uses
3. Barren and unculturable land
4. Permanent pastures and other grazing lands
5. Land under miscellaneous tree crops and groves
6. Culturable wasteland
7. Fallow lands other than current fallows
8. Current fallows
9. Net area sown

These nine categories add up to the total reporting area. Out of these nine categories, following two categories are not taken into account in estimating the extent of wastelands in this chapter :—

(i) Area put to non-agricultural use and

(ii) Land under miscellaneous tree crops and groves.

Category (i) includes, the townships, village habitations, roads, etc. Although there is a strong possibility that some areas within the cities and townships will be in a highly degraded state, their problems are very different in nature and will not have a significant impact on land use pattern. Also, save for an actual survey, it will be very difficult to indirectly estimate the degraded areas in this category. This category has therefore been excluded from consideration in this chapter.

Category (ii) above, as the name suggests, is under various tree crops and groves. These areas, though capable of giving better economic returns do not pose any ecological hazards. Since the emphasis in this chapter is on those wastelands which are affected by specific problems and not on the economic potential of such lands, it seems reasonable to exclude this category from consideration.

Section IV : Problem-Categories

Having excluded the above-mentioned two categories of land use, the objective now is to estimate from the remaining seven categories, the areas affected by various problems. It has already been pointed out in Section I that there are a number of problems afflicting various regions. They are enumerated here—

- sheet erosion
- ravines
- waterlogging
- riverine lands
- shifting cultivation
- gully erosion, stream bank erosion

- salinity and alkalinity
- shifting sand dunes
- wind erosion
- extreme moisture stress
- coastal sand dunes.

It is quite clear that these problems cut across the seven categories of land use which are being considered in this chapter. One of the basic problems in proper estimation of the extent of wastelands arises in establishing one to one correspondence between the problem-categories and land use categories. As a first step in eliminating this problem all the problems afflicting various regions have been reclassified into three broad categories :

(a) Water erosion includes sheet erosion, ravines, riverine lands, waterlogging, gully erosion, shifting cultivation etc.

(b) Wind erosion includes shifting sand dunes, wind erosion, extreme moisture stress, coastal sand dunes etc.

(c) Salinity and alkalinity

Section V : Relationship Between Land Use Classes and Problem-Categories

Now, it needs to be ascertained if any of the above-mentioned problem-categories directly correspond to land use categories. In this connection following observations are made —

(i) The area affected by 'salinity and alkalinity' are usually put under the category 'barren and unculturable land' in land use surveys. This category also includes cold deserts, mountainous and rocky regions etc.[4] There is, however, no technological option in reclaiming these lands and hence the problem of cold deserts or rocky areas are not being considered here. But, it will be reasonable to assume that there is one-to-two correspondence between problem category, 'salinity and alkalinity' and land use category 'barren and unculturable land'. Although there will be some area affected by 'salinity and alkalinity' in the land use category 'forests', there exists no record of distribution of such lands in forest area. Forests, however, are being treated as a separate category. Therefore, it will be logical to estimate the incidence of 'salinity and alkalinity' in the land use category 'barren and unculturable land' only.

(ii) The remaining two problem-categories 'water erosion' and 'wind-erosion' do not have one-to-two correspondence with any of the land use 'categories. In fact, they cut across all the categories.

The relationship between the redefined three problem-categories and the seven land use categories which are being considered in this chapter can be depicted by the following matrix:

*Land-use category according to the Directorate of Economics & Statistics, Ministry of Agriculture	Problem category		
	Water Erosion	*Wind Erosion*	*Salinity & Alkalinity*
1. Forests			
2. Barren and unculturable land			
3. Permanent pastures and other grazing lands			
4. Culturable waste			
5. Fallows other than current fallows			
6. Current fallows			
7. Net area sown			

* Two other land use categories, *viz.*, 'Area put to agricultural use' and 'land under miscellaneous tree crops and groves' have been excluded from consideration in this chapter for the reasons mentioned earlier.

Section VI : Mthodology

It will be clear from this matrix that the task now is—

(i) to determine the area under forests affected by water erosion, wind erosion, salinity and alkalinity;

(ii) to determine the area affected by salinity and alkalinity in the land use category 'barren and unculturable land'.

(iii) to determine the areas affected by water erosion and wind erosion in land use categories 3 to 7.

The land use category 'forests' is fraught with very different kind of problems and is dealt with at the end of this section. Before estimating the extent of wastelands under each problem-category, the following observations about some of the land use categories are relevant—

> There are a number of reports and documents to suggest that areas under the land use category 'permanent pastures and other grazing lands', 'culturable waste' and 'fallows other than current fallows' are some of the most degraded lands. It would be sufficient to substantiate this observation with the following extract from the report of National Commission on Agriculture[5] — "The magnitudes of 'culturable lands' and 'fallow lands other than current follows' indicate neglected land management. These areas are liable to erosion. The areas categorised as "permanent pastures and other grazing lands" covering about 13 million hectares perhaps represent, fallaciously though, some of the worst eroded areas." In the light of these observations it is quite clear that all the lands under these land use categories should be taken as wastelands. The distribution of these lands between the categories wind eroded and water eroded still needs to be determined.
>
> The land use category 'barren and unculturable land' has already been discussed and it was observed that the area affected by 'salinity and alkalinity' will be assumed to be exclusively found in this category. This leaves only one land use category 'net area sown' to be considered. The incidence of degradation in net sown area is affected by three factors— (i) rainfall, (ii) irrigated/unirrigated cultivation, and (iii) type of crop. It is also affected by the topography. However, in the absence of precise data on this aspect, it is not considered here. The above-mentioned factors are taken into account while considering the incidence of

wastelands in the land use category 'net area sown'. The exact distribution of this area between 'wind eroded' and 'water eroded' categories is discussed later.

Keeping these observations about land use categories in view, the methodology adopted in estimation of the extent of wastelands under each problem-category is explained here.

(a) Areas affected by Salinity and Alkalinity

The area affected by salinity and alkalinity has been fairly accurately estimated by Central Soil Salinity Research Institute, Karnal.[6] Their estimate has been accepted and used in this chapter with the following assumptions:

- The area under saline and alkaline soils as estimated by them will be found exclusively in the land use category 'barren and unculturable land'.
- The saline and alkaline area in the land use category 'forests' are not included here. The relevant figures are given in Table 12.1. Table 12.2 gives the distribution of salt-affected soils between the categories 'Saline soils' and 'Alkaline soils'.

(b) Area affected by Wind Erosion

The problem of wind erosion (sand dunes, extreme moisture stress, coastal sand dunes etc.) is prevalent—

- along the long coast line of about 5,600 kms and
- in the hot desert areas of Indian arid zone.

The problem in the coastal regions is two-fold :

- that of salinity and
- sand dunes.

Table 12.1 : Estimate of Saline and Alkaline lands in the land use category 'barren and unculturable land'

States/U.T.s	*Saline & Alkaline lands (hectares in lacs)*	
Andhra Pradesh	2.40	
Assam	–	
Bihar	0.04	
Gujarat	12.14	
Haryana	5.26	
Himachal Pradesh	–	
Jammu & Kashmir	–	
Karnataka	5.04	
Kerala	0.16	
Madhya Pradesh	2.42	
Maharashtra	5.34	
Manipur	–	
Meghalaya	–	
Nagaland	–	
Orissa	4.04	
Punjab	6.88	
Rajasthan	7.28	
Sikkim	–	
Tamil Nadu	0.04	
Tripura	–	
Uttar Pradesh	12.95	
West Bengal	0.50	
U.T.s		0.16
	Total 64.65	

Table 12.2 : Distribution of salt-affected soils between the categories 'Saline Soils' and 'Alkaline soils'

Broad Group	*States in which the soils occur (hectares in lacs)*	
1. Coastal saline soils		
a. Coastal saline soils of arid regions	Gujarat	7.14
b. Deltaic saline soils on the humid regions	West Bengal, Orissa, Andhra Pradesh & Tamil Nadu	13.94
c. Acid saline soils	Kerala	0.16
2. Saline soils of the medium and deep black soil regions	Karnataka, Madhya Pradesh, Andhra Pradesh, Maharashtra	14.20
3. Saline soils of the arid and semi-arid regions.	Gujarat, Rajasthan, Punjab, Haryana and Uttar Pradesh	10.00
4. Sodic (Alkaline, Usar) soils of the Indo-Gangetic Plains	Haryana, Punjab, Uttar Pradesh, Bihar, Rajasthan and Madhya Pradesh	25.00
	Total	**70.44**

The part of coastal region affected by salinity has been already accounted for in (a) above. However, the part affected by sand dunes needs to be estimated. There are indications that the problem of sand dunes in the coastal regions has received proper attention in the States of Tamil Nadu and Orissa. It is stated that "plantation of Casuarina on the sandy foreshores backed by coconut, cashewnut, Eucalyptus farther in land can considerably minimise the problem of blown sand as Tamil Nadu experience has shown."[7] The same report mentions elsewhere that "Orissa has done a lot of work in the reclamation of the sandy coastal areas by providing a wind break of .... These plantations have been very effective........... Large-scale reclamation of the coastal tracts along these lines is suggested."[8] It is very difficult to make even good judgements about other States. However, the problem areas in coastal regions which have not yet been reclaimed and are as yet not accounted for in this chapter will be comparatively small. This can be explained by Fig. 12.1.

The shaded area has either been accounted for in the category 'salinity and alkalinity' or has been reclaimed as in the States of Tamil Nadu and Orissa. The only area that has not been accounted for is the non-shaded portion in the Fig.12.1. Considering that the total area in coastal regions is approximately 5.6 million hectares, the problem area will not be more than 60 per cent. Out of this, considerable portion has been accounted for. Therefore, the problem area that is not taken into consideration will not be more than 1 to 2 million hectares. In the absence of any other definite data, it has been decided not to take this problem area in the estimate of wastelands. To that extent these estimates are on lower side.

Fig. 12. 1: Problem area in coastal regions

Salinity
Sand dune
West Bengal
Andhra Pradesh
Karnataka
Kerala
Maharashtra
Gujarat
Tamil Nadu
Orissa

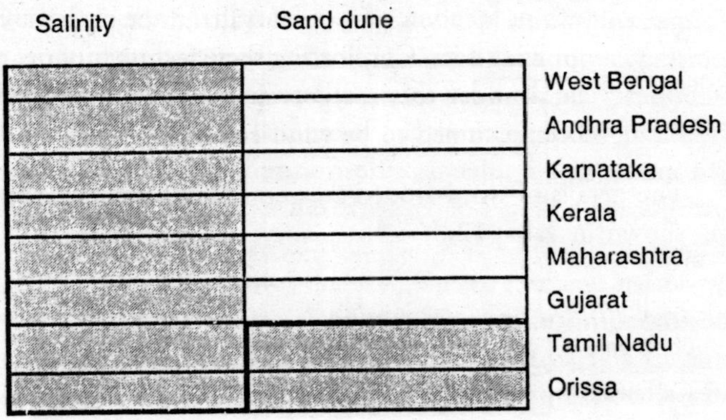

Keeping the above in view, the only area that is affected by wind erosion and is considered in this chapter is hot deserts of Indian arid zone. This area consists of 11 western districts of Rajasthan, three districts each of Gujarat and Haryana. The portion of this area affected by wind erosion is calculated in the following manner :

(1) Firstly, the area of this region under all the land use categories has been calculated district-wise.

(2) The area in all the 17 districts, falling under the land use categories 'permanent pastures and other grazing lands', 'culturable wastes' and 'fallows other than current fallows' has been assumed to be 100 per cent wind eroded for the reasons mentioned earlier.

(3) Fifty per cent of the area under the land use category 'current fallows' in these 17 districts has been assumed to be wind-eroded. Mainly because of the definition of the term 'current fallows', it seems, some of the good lands where the cultivation has not been practised for the last three seasons have been designated to be so. It is specifically to account for such lands that only 50 per cent of this category has been assumed to be degraded.

(4) All the land in these seventeen districts falling under the land-use category 'Net Area Sown' has low rainfall and except for a very small percentage of this land in Haryana, which is irrigated, most of this area is non-irrigated. Again, except for some part in Haryana, none of this area is paddy growing area. Considering these factors fifty per cent of the land under this category in these seventeen districts has been assumed to be wind-eroded.

The details of wind-eroded area on the basis of these assumptions are shown in Table 12.3.

(c) Area affected by water erosion

Area affected by water erosion is calculated in the following manner :

Table 12.3 : Details of wind-eroded regions in India (Non-Forest only)

State/ Districts	*Net Area Sown*	*P. & G.*	*C.W.*	*Fallows*	*Current Fallows*
1	*2*	*3*	*4*	*5*	*6*
Rajasthan					
1. Bikaner	2.91	0.42	14.27	1.65	1.24
2. Jaisalmer	7.45	0.89	34.84	0.77	0.06
3. Barmer	1.51	2.12	3.75	2.87	2.21
4. Jodhpur	4.26	1.12	0.09	4.74	2.30
5. Nagaur	5.51	0.73	0.03	0.96	2.84
6. Churu	3.38	0.47	0.44	1.28	1.37
7. Pali	1.15	0.92	0.16	1.31	1.40
8. Jalore	2.45	0.51	0.06	1.07	1.08
9. Ganganagar	1.21	0.22	2.50	0.35	0.62
10. Jhunjhunu	3.00	0.45	0.05	0.17	0.32
11. Sikar	4.88	0.48	0.14	0.46	0.74
Total	**37.71**	**8.33**	**56.33**	**15.63**	**14.18**
Gujarat					
1. Mehsana	6.96	0.56	0.27	0.12	0.26
2. Banaskantha	8.21	0.72	0.37	0.11	0.60
3. Kutch	3.00	0.70	1.80	1.60	0.45
Total	**18.17**	**1.98**	**2.44**	**1.83**	**1.31**
Haryana					
1. Bhiwani	4.51	0.08	–	–	0.05
2. Hissar	5.42	–	–	–	0.29
3. Rohtak	3.27	–	0.15	–	0.08
Total	**13.20**	**0.08**	**0.15**	–	**0.42**
Grand Total	**69.08**	**10.39**	**58.92**	**17.46**	**15.91**

Wind-eroded area : Net sown area (50 %) 34.54
P. & G. (100%) 10.39
C.W. (100%) 58.92
Fallow (110%) 17.46
Current Fallows (50%) 7.95

Total : 129.26

(1) The area under all the classes of land use in the seventeen districts assumed to be affected by wind erosion has been deducted from the nation-wide land use classification. The remainder is the relevant area from which the extent of 'water-eroded' region can be estimated. This also maintains the exclusivity of problem categories.

(2) The land use categories 'forests' and 'barren and unculturable land' are not being considered here for the reasons mentioned earlier.

(3) Out of the remaining land use categories 'Permanent pastures and other grazing lands', 'culturable waste' and fallows other than current fallows' and fifty per cent of the area falling under the category 'current fallows' has been assumed to be 'water-eroded' for the same reasons which are mentioned earlier. The details of these wastelands are shown in Table 12.4 under the title 'Estimate of Wastelands affected by Water Erosion in Uncultivated Area.'

(4) To calculate the water-eroded lands in cultivated area, only the unirrigated net sown area has been taken into account. "Irrigated areas are considered to be properly levelled and shaped so that they are subject to minimal erosion."[9] The unirrigated area has been segregated into two categories—
- high and medium rainfall area (above 750 mm).
- low rainfall area (below 750 mm).

For both of these categories, further sub-divisions are made into areas growing paddy and those which are growing non-paddy crops. It has been further assumed that the entire cultivated land in low rainfall area is non-paddy growing. This assumption is justified as only non-irrigated lands are being considered here. The estimate of water-eroded area is then made by assuming that fifty per cent of unirrigated non-paddy area and 10 per cent of unirrigated paddy area is affected by water erosion in the High and Medium rainfall areas.[10] The precarious condition of agriculture in the unirrigated high and medium rainfall area justifies the assumption of fifty per cent of non-paddy area being

Table 12.4 : Estimate of Wastelands affected by water erosion in uncultivated area ('000 ha.)

States/ U.T.s	*Current fallows*	*50%of Col. 2*	*Permanent pastures and Grazing*	**Culturable Waste*	*Fallows other than current fallows*	*Area affected by water erosion (Total of Cols. 3+4+5+6)*
Andhra Pradesh	2234	1117	948	888	1053	4006
Assam	108	54	185	130	122	491
Bihar	1619	809	144	468	924	2345
Gujarat*	354	177	652	1758	231	2818
Haryana*	28	14	43	21	–	78
Himachal Pradesh	49	24	1024	136	4	1188
Jammu & Kashmir	86	43	124	149	8	324
Karnataka	967	483	1398	530	623	3034
Kerala	42	21	6	123	27	177
Madhya Pradesh	858	429	2877	1849	933	6088
Maharashtra	812	406	1492	1021	843	3762
Manipur	–	–	–	–	–	–
Meghalaya	51	25	17	455	261	758
Nagaland	84	42	–	–	426	468
Orissa	531	265	534	260	138	1197
Punjab	55	27	3	48	–	78
Rajasthan*	521	260	1001	1249	555	3065
Sikkim	–	–	103	1	1	105
Tamil Nadu	1267	633	161	362	448	1604
Tripura	2	1	–	–	2	3
Uttar Pradesh	932	466	298	1338	607	2709
West Bengal	–	–	–	–	212	212
U.T.s	209	104	14	268	381	767
Total	**10809**	**5400**	**11024**	**11054**	**7799**	**35277**

degraded. However, assuming 10 per cent of non-irrigated paddy area as water-eroded in this rainfall category may be questioned. It is stated that "the area under rainfed rice which is levelled, shaped and adequately bunded for holding water is also well protected from the eroding influence of rainfall."[11] Contrary to general belief, not all rainfed paddy cultivation is practised by bunding the land, specially in uplands. Therefore, it is quite reasonable to assume 10 per cent of such area to be subject to water-erosion. As far as low rainfall area is concerned 40 per cent has been assuned to be water-eroded. Low rainfall area are very dependent on the vagaries of monsoon and therefore most farmers do not invest large funds in bunding and proper management of the land

Table 12.5 : Estimate of degraded lands in non-irrigated cultivated area ('000 ha.) (affected by water erosion)

States/U.Ts	High & Medium Total	Rainfall area Non paddy	Paddy	Degraded Area (50% non paddy +10% paddy)	Low rainfall Area Total	Degraded 40%	Total degraded area (5+7)
Andhra Pradesh	4470	4248	222	2146.2	3224	1289.6	3435.8
Assam	2107	833	1274	543.9	–	–	543.9
Bihar	5572	2474	3098	1546.8	–	–	1546.8
Gujarat	2442	2163	279	1109.4	3269	1307.6	2417.0
Haryana	168	136	32	100.0	244	97.6	197.6
Himachal Pradesh	472	472	–	236.0	–	–	236.0
Jammu & Kashmir	389	389	–	194.5	30	12.0	206.5
Karnataka	2831	2422	409	1251.9	6075	2430.0	3681.9
Kerala	1976	1657	319	860.4	–	–	860.4
Madhya Pradesh	15989	12003	3986	6400.1	543	217.2	6617.3
Maharashtra	10644	9544	1100	4882.0	5705	2282.0	7164.0
Manipur	75	16	59	13.9	–	–	13.9
Meghalaya	145	105	40	56.5	–	–	56.5
Nagaland	96	77	19	40.4	–	–	40.4
Orissa	4949	2652	2297	1555.7	–	–	1555.7
Punjab	338	300	38	153.8	577	230.8	384.6
Rajasthan	1246	1115	131	570.6	7559	3023.6	3594.2
Sikkim	51	51	–	25.5	–	–	25.5
Tamil Nadu	3378	3189	189	1783.5	–	–	1783.5
Tripura	217	179	38	103.3	–	–	103.3
Uttar Pradesh	8061	4033	4028	2419.3	529	211.6	2630.9
West Bangal	4050	1775	2275	1115.0	–	–	1115.0
U.T.s	336	168	168	100.8	12	4.8	105.6
Total	**70002**	**50001**	**20001**	**27209.5**	**27767**	**11106.8**	**38316.3**

and therefore it seems reasonable to assume 40 per cent of such lands to be water-eroded. The details of water-eroded area in cultivated land are given in Table 12.5.

After including the wind-eroded cultivated area, the total eroded cultivated area works out to be approximately 41.5 million hectares. This is much lower than the figure of 70 million hectares[12], mentioned in the report of National Commission on Agriculture. However, the discrepancy is explicable. The Report published in 1976, uses the figures of land treated with soil conservation measures up to Fourth Plan only. This figure up to Fourth Plan works out to be 15 million hectares. But, till 1979-80, an area of 23.40 million hectares was treated by various soil conservation measures[13] and the Sixth Plan aimed at a target of "an additional 7.1 million hectares on the base of 23.4 million hectares."[14] Now that the plan has been under implementation for past three years, one can assume additional 3.5 million hectares being so treated. Thus, from the 70 million hectares estimated by National Commission on Agriculture, one can safely deduct about 11.4 million hectares. Also, there must be a number of cultivators who would have taken suitable conservation measures on their own and for which no records exist. Considering these factors, the gap between the estimates of National Commission on Agriculture and this chapter does not seem to be so large as it apparently looks to be.

(d) Degraded area under forests

The estimation of degraded lands in land use category 'Forests' is a very difficult task. The task is made more difficult by various ways of classifying forests. Using different classifications, earlier estimates have been very different from each other. Thus, the Forest Research Institute, Dehra Dun, using the legal classification of forests into reserved, protected and unclassed forests arrives at a figure of 17.6 million hectares of degraded forests. It is mentioned that "Reserved and protected forests constitute permanent forest estates, maintained for the purpose of producing timber and other produce and for protective reasons. As such they fall within the category of 'permanent forests' as used by the Food and Agriculture Organisation in its World Forest Inventory. Unclassed forests are largely degraded and unprofitable forests, rarely surveyed or subject to any organised protection or management"... "Unclassed forests........ 1,76,630 sq. kms (68,195 sq. miles) forming 22.6 per cent of the total forest area."[15]

Using another classification of the forests putting them into the categories of 'merchantable' and 'inaccessible' another estimate puts the figure of degraded forests to be 25 million hectares. "Of the 75 million hectares of forests about 15 million hectares are unproductive being inaccessible... of the balance 60 million hectares, only about 35 million hectares are well wooded and the balance 25 million hectares are either partially stocked or are completely denuded of tree growth..."[16] In a document published by the Department of Environment, the degraded area in forests is estimated to be almost half of the total forest area. "...no more than 12 per cent of the country's land surface, or less than half of the 75 million hectares classed as forest lands in revenue records, is actually under adequate tree cover."[17] However, on the basis of this report, one cannot assume that 50 per cent of forest area in every State will be uniformly degraded.

It will be clear from the above that there seems to be no ready indirect method to estimate the incidence of wastelands in forest area. The only scientific alternative seems to be interpretation of landsat imagery figures in the land use category 'forests'. Because of these reasons, this chapter is restricting the estimation of the extent of wastelands to non-forest area only.

Section VII : The Estimate

Based on the methodology discussed above, the area affected by salinity and alkalinity works out to be 7.16 million hectares (Table 12.1). The distribution between Saline and Alkaline lands is shown in Table 12.2. The area affected by wind erosion is estimated to be 12.92 million hectares (Table 12.3). The area affected by water erosion in uncultivated area is given in Table 12.4 and is estimated to be 3.38 million hectares, while water-eroded areas in cultivated area are estimated to be 38.21 million hectares (Table 12.5).

Table 12.6 : Estimate of Wastelands in India (Non-forest area only)

States/U.T.s	*Saline & Alkaline lands*	*Wind-eroded area*	*Water-eroded*	*Total area*
Andhra Pradesh	2.40	–	74.42	76.82
Assam	–	–	9.35	9.35
Bihar	0.04	–	38.92	38.96
Gujarat	12.14	7.04	52.35	71.53
Haryana	5.26	15.99	2.76	24.01
Himachal Pradesh	–	–	14.24	14.24
Jammu & Kashmir	–	–	5.31	5.31
Karnataka	4.04	–	67.18	71.22
Kerala	0.16	–	10.37	10.53
Madhya Pradesh	2.42	–	127.05	129.47
Maharashtra	5.34	–	110.26	115.60
Manipur	–	–	0.14	0.14
Meghalaya	–	–	8.15	8.15
Nagaland	–	–	5.08	5.08
Orissa	4.04	–	27.53	31.57
Punjab	6.88	–	4.63	11.51
Rajasthan	7.28	106.23	66.59	180.01
Sikkim	–	–	1.31	1.31
Tamil Nadu	0.04	–	33.88	33.92
Tripura	–	–	1.08	1.08
Uttar Pradesh	12.95	–	53.40	66.35
West Bengal	8.50	–	13.27	21.77
U.T.s	0.16	–	8.73	8.89
Total	**71.65**	**129.26**	**736.00**	**936.82**

A comprehensive data of wastelands in non-forest area according to problem categories is given in Table 12.6. The total wastelands in non-forest area are estimated to be 93.69 million hectares. Since these estimates maintain the exclusivity of land categories and there is no overlapping of problem-categories also, they can be presented according to the land use categories also. This is done in Table 12.7.

Table 12.7 : Estimate of Wastelands according to Land-use categories (Non-Forest)
(in lakh hectare)

States/U.T.s	*Barren & unculturable*	*P. & G.*	*C.W.*	*Fallows other than C.F.*	*Current Fallows*	*Net area Sown*
Andhra Pradesh	2.40	9.48	8.88	10.53	11.17	34.36
Assam	–	1.85	1.30	1.22	0.54	4.44
Bihar	0.04	1.44	4.68	9.24	8.09	15.49
Gujarat	12.14	8.05	20.02	4.14	2.43	24.17
Haryana	5.26	0.51	0.36	–	0.35	1.98
Himachal Pradesh	–	10.24	1.36	0.04	0.24	2.36
Jammu & Kashmir	–	1.24	1.49	0.08	0.43	2.07
Karnataka	4.04	13.98	5.30	6.25	4.83	36.82
Kerala	0.16	0.06	1.23	0.27	0.21	8.60
Madhya Pradesh	2.42	28.77	18.49	9.33	4.29	66.17
Maharashtra	5.34	15.92	10.21	8.43	4.06	71.64
Manipur	–	–	–	–	–	0.14
Meghalaya	–	0.17	4.55	2.61	0.25	0.57
Nagaland	–	–	–	4.26	0.42	0.40
Orissa	4.04	5.34	2.60	1.38	2.65	15.56
Punjab	6.88	0.03	0.48	–	0.27	3.85
Rajasthan	7.28	18.34	68.82	21.18	9.69	35.94
Sikkim	–	1.03	0.01	0.01	–	0.26
Tamil Nadu	0.04	1.61	3.62	4.48	6.33	17.84
Tripura	–	–	0.02	0.02	0.01	1.03
Uttar Pradesh	12.95	2.98	13.38	6.07	4.66	26.31
West Bengal	8.50	–	–	2.12	–	11.15
U.T.s	0.16	0.14	2.68	3.81	1.04	1.06
Total	**71.65**	**121.18**	**169.48**	**95.47**	**61.96**	**382.21**

NOTES

1. The Report of National Commission on Agriculture, Vol 5, p. 178.
2. "Soil Conservation, Problem, App.oach and Progress in India', Ministry of Agriculture, Department of Agriculture and Cooperation, Soil and Water Conservation Division, New Delhi, 1982, p. 2 & 3.
3. Shri B.B. Vohra quotes a figure of 200 m hectares which is arrived at by adding 25 m hectares (affected by floods and waterlogging and salinity due to irrigation) to the estimate of Ministry of Agriculture. Since the estimate of Ministry of Agriculture itself suffers from the error of overlapping of categories, the estimate of Vohra is obviously more inflated.
   —*A Policy for Land and Water*, Shri B. B. Vohra, Sardar Patel Memorial Lectures 1980, Department of Environment, Government of India.
4. Another 21 m.h. are classified as barren and unculturable, perhaps for certain intrinsic disabilities such as these lands being perpetually snowbound or rocky

in nature', Shri B. B. Vohra — Sardar Patel Memorial Lectures 1980 — 'A Policy for Land and Water', Department of Environment, Government of India, p. 2.
5. The Report of National Commission on Agriculture, Vol. IX, p. 126.
6. I.P. Abrol, K.S. Dargan, D.R. Bhumbla — 'Reclaiming Alkali Soils' — Central Soil Salinity Research Institute, Karnal, 1973, p. 4.
7. The Report of National Commission on Agriculture, Vol.V., p. 197.
8. *Ibid.*, p. 211.
9. Report of the National Commission on Agriculture, Vol. V., p. 233.
10. The area under land use category 'Net Sown Area' in the 17 districts affected by wind erosion has been entirely deducted from this subdivision. It has been assumed that all these districts fall in low-rainfall area. Actual rainfall data substantiate it.
11. Report of National Commission on Agriculture, Vol.V., p. 233-34. .
12. *Ibid.*, p. 234.
13. Sixth Five Year Plan: Planning Commission, p. 103.
14. *Ibid.*, p. 103.
15. *100 Years of Indian Forestry,* Vol I., Forest Research Institute, Dehradun, p. 141.
16. S.R. Bhagwat : *How to increase Productivity of Our Forests: National Seminar on Forests and Environment,* 1981, Bangalore, sponsored by Karnataka Forest Department, p. 46.
17. Recommendations Regarding the Revision of The National Forest Policy, Department of Environment, Government of India, New Delhi, p. 1.

13

Soils of Wastelands and their Potentials in Arid Western Rajasthan

A. S. Kolarkar and *R. P. Dhir*

In our country, where arable farming, for long, has been considered a prime use of land, a land which is thought to be capable of supporting agriculture but is not being so used is named a "Culturable wasteland" or often referred to simply as wasteland. Other lands marked in revenue records as forest, permanent pastures, plantation crops etc., since not cultivated are excluded from its purview. Excluded are also those lands which do not support sustained agriculture yet are cultivated and those which can support some kind of useful vegetation but are presently near barren condition. The latter one are often referred to as "Banjar". Therefore, with this old land use terminology, in the context of rehabilitating the wastelands to meet the environmental and energy requirements, there has been diverse opinions on the definition of the word "Waste land". However, keeping objectives in the mind, it can pragmatically be defined as "land lying idle, unused, uncultivated and sparsely inhabited by useful vegetation.

According to the revenue statistics, arid zone of Rajasthan is shown to have over 5 million hectares of wastelands which amounts to one-third of area of such lands in the country. However, with experience gained during resources surveys in this region covering 1,40,000 sq.km, it seems to us that the classifsication of these lands as wastelands needs a rethinking. This is so, for two reasons. Firstly, because many of these lands are not idle or unused lands. Rather these lands have been excessively grazed in the past and their present state of deterioration to near barrenness is primarily due to this overexploitation. Secondly, because of severe climatic limitations, these lands cannot be put to a more intensive land use like arable farming except for a small fraction which will receive irrigation from the Indira Gandhi Canal. Therefore, it would be more prudent to treat the so-called wastelands as degraded pasture lands which with some techno-economic input can be made to produce substantially more to meet the growing needs of the society than what is being realised at present.

Arid Zone Research over the past two decades has given us a set of technologies for rehabilitating these lands, However, the precise measures to be adopted including choice of species, nature of land treatments etc., are dictated by the site characteristics like the landform, surface slope, depth and moisture retention capacity of soil, salinity and erodibility and so on. Present chapter describes the soils of major wastelands of the region emphasising specifically their behavioural characteristics for improved management.

Brief description of the soils of the wastelands

The wastelands possess a large diversity ranging from the deep sandy soils of the dunes through shallow soils of desert plains to rocky pediments and plateau. In other situations salinity is the prime limiting factor. A brief description of these soils together with their extent and distribution are given in the following text, whereas their laboratory characterisitics are summed up in Table 13.1.

Soils of the duny and hummocky sandy plains

These soils cover nearly 3.5 million ha. By far the major occurrence of these is in Bikaner and Jaisalmer districts followed by Barmer and Ganganagar districts. The landform is made up of dunes and hummocky plains. The soils are very deep fine sandy with a clay content ranging from 1.8 to 4.5 per cent and silt from 1.2 to 5.6 per cent. Fine sand is the dominant fraction. The soils are calcareous with small amount of finely dispersed calcium carbonate. The soils have a very high infiltration rate with moisture equivalent values of around 3.5 to 5 per cent. The

Table 13.1 : General fertility status of various wasteland soils of desert region

	Kind of waste-land soils	*Major available plant nutrients*			*Available micro nutrients(ppm)*			
		Organic carbon (%)	P_2O_5 *(kg/ha)*	K_2O *(kg/ha)*	*Fe*	M_n	C_u	Z_n
1.	Soils of duny and hummocky sandy plains	0.049 (0.0039-0.09)	9.4 (5-22)	158 (80-356)	10.75 (5.2-19.3)	3.63 (1.8-7.4)	0.782 (0.39-1.2)	0.42 (0.21-0.93)
2.	Hard pan soils	0.063 (0.049-0.077)	11.0 (8-14)	343 (290-376)	5.71 (3.8-7.6)	9.10 (5.4-12.5)	0.596 (0.45-1.0)	0.82 (0.5-1.1)
3.	Shallow gravelly soils of gently sloping plains	0.277 (0.245-0.309)	12 (9-15)	261 (243-279)	5.41 (3.4-7.2)	10.76 (6.8-16.2)	0.622 (0.48-0.90)	1.00 (0.48-1.3)
4.	Soils of low hills and undulating gravelly plains	0.138 (0.09-0.19)	13 (9-17)	247 (190-336)	6.4 (3.18-9.8)	11.22 (3.8-15.2)	0.79 (0.4-0.8)	1.10 (0.7-1.66)
5.	Hills and gravelly piedmonts	0.115 (0.110-0.120)	12 (10-14)	93 (66-120)	4.25 (3.4-5.8)	11.68 (10.0-13.6)	0.68 (0.58-0.80)	0.99 (0.58-1.80)
6.	Salt-affected soils	0.261 (0.08-0.528)	16 (5-41)	308 (115-627)	9.95 (3.0-16.0)	12.88 (5.6-17.0)	1.18 (0.55-2.00)	1.10 (0.56-3.37)

Note: Figures indicate the mean values and those in brackets indicate the range.

soils can retain 45 to 70 mm of water per meter depth. The soils are structureless and lack any aggregation and are, therefore, highly erodible. Unless protected by vegetation, a massive movement and redistribution of sands can take place on these soils in response to strong winds. A recent study has shown that 0.3 to 0.8 meter deep blow out hollows and formation of transverse ridges and shrub coppice mounds can occur on these lands during years of unusually strong wind regime. As much as 400 to 1200 tons of soil gets reworked in the process from each hectare of land.

It will be seen from the data presented in Table 10.1, the soils have a mean organic carbon value of 0.05 per cent which appears low. The available phosphorus content varies from 5 to 22 kg/ha and available K_2O. from 80 to 356 kg/ha. The data also show that the soils are well provided with various micro-nutrient elements.

Though the soils have low moisture retention capacity, yet these possess a distinct advantage in their very low values of unsaturated state hudraulic conductivity. This property is very helpful in conserving the stored moisture from unproductive evaporation losses.. The soils also provide ample opportunity for a rapid proliferation of the root system. Experience also shows that the fertility status of these soils is not a limiting factor in establishment and maintenance of a healthy vegetation cover at a near optimum such as is permitted by the limited rainfall of the tract. In other words, these lands can be maintained at a satisfactory productivity level without the need or costly soil fertility building inputs. Of course, their erodibility is a serious factor to be recknoned with but fortunately both the soil conservation needs as well as climate constraint permit the maintenance of a grass vegetation cover only. Therefore, once an optimum vegetation cover is established on these lands, under a proper grazing policy, wind erosion should not be a serious problem. In parts of Jodhpur and Nagaur, where mean annual rainfall is 300 to 400 mrn, silvi-pastoral land use is ideal. The associated trees by feeding primarily on the deeply percolated moisture, provide additional fodder while introducing some degree of stability to the production.

Hard Pan Soils

These soils are spread over an area of approximately 0.13 million hectares in the districts of Bikaner, Jodhpur and Jaisalmer. The soils have a depth of 15 to 35 cm which is followed by a strongly developed, often indurated lime concretionary/gravelly strata. In about 5 to 10 per cent of the area the indurated strata is exposed at the surface. The soils have a flat to gently sloping surface. The texture of the soil is generally loamy fine sands. The solum proper can retain 20 to 40 mm of moisture. The underlying strata is only slowly permeable to roots and moisture. Nevertheless, the sub-strata is helpful in providing some moisture during the prolonged dry season. The soil possesses a serious root zone limitation for trees like Khejri but *Zizyphus* and *Capparis* can still grow on these lands. However, these lands are well suited for development of grasslands though the productivity is not as that on the deep soils. Experience at CAZRI has shown that *Cenchrus ciliaris, C. setigerus* and *Eleusine compressa* can establish well. *Lasiurus sindicus* can also grow with some care.

Shallow Gravelly soils of Gently Sloping Plains

These lands occupy nearly 1.7 million ha mainly in the Jaisalmer and Bikaner distircts and to a lesser extent in Jodhpur and Barmer districts. The surface of these soils is strewn with gravels and cobbles to the extent of 5 to 20 per cent of soil mass. Besides, there are patches where the percentage of gravels may be as high as 70 per cent. The solum which has a depth of 10 to 40 cm has also some gravel mixed in the soil. The underlying strata is often gravelly or concretionary which is locally indurated. The landform unit also contains exposure of low hills or flat rocks.

The gravel free soil has a texture ranging from fine sands to fine sandy loam with a clay content 7 to 13 per cent. The silt content is 6 to 11 per cent. The soils can retain 15 to 35 mm of moisture in the solum. The soils have a reasonably good amount of plant nutrients.

The lands tend to form a crust. This factor together with the gravel component cause a significant run-off. Therefore, contour furrowing/trenching is desirable. Soil working is also necessary prior to reseeding. With these practices the lands can be made to support a substantially greater vegetation cover than that at present

Soils of low hills and undulating gravelly plains

These lands occur primarily in the Jaisalmer district where they occupy approximately 0.5 million hectares. The slopes are complex and have a range of 2 to 6 per cent. The surface is littered with gravels of varying sizes and lithology. The fine earth fraction is also variable in texture but is mostly loamy sand to fine sandy loam. There are also a few exposures of rocks. The soils as can be seen from data in Table 13.1 have a satisfactory fertility level.

Presently, these lands have a very thin vegetation cover that is dominated by annual grasses and herbs. Since this vegetation lasts for a very short period, the land carry a barren look almost during whole of the year.

These lands are prone to crust formation. Presence of gravel in the solum is another adverse factor. But the main limiting factor is paucity of rainfall as these lands lie in those areas which receive the lowest mean annual rainfall in the region. These features make the rehabilitation of these lands a most challenging task.

Hills and gravelly piedmonts

This unit comprises hills and dissected plateau with rugged, steep slopes. Also included are associated gravelly piedmont. These mostly occur as isolated features amidst alluvial and sandy plains. The hill slopes, particularly those in rhyolites are extremely rugged and devoid of any soil cover. However, granites often have some hollows, cavities or crevices where gravel and some fine earth fraction are present to provide a niche for hardy plants. The dissected sandstone plateau are also rugged though often fractured. The piedmonts have slopes of 5 to 15 per cent and are made up of an admixture of gravels and earthy fraction. Therefore, moisture retention capacity, even though the depth of sediment is meter or more, is low. It is only in the bed of runnels where supplemental moisture is available that some vegetation cover is present. However, with due care a sparse cover of hardy species like *Acacia senegal* and *Prosopis juliflora* with short grass like *Aristida* can be established on the piedmont slopes. For establishment of trees pit or box trench method of planting coupled with run-off intercepting devices are highly desirable.

Salt affected soils

Though isolated saline depressions lie scattered in major part of arid Rajasthan, the major area of occurrence of salt-affected soils lies in the south-eastern part in Pali, Jodhpur and Jalore districts. A survey conducted in the area has mapped 0.44 million hectares of primary saline soils.

These occur as irregular shaped patches of varying sizes, ranging from 50 to 2500 ha, in association with normal soils. Actually, the surface salinity is only the proverbial tip of the iceberg, there being far greater mass of salinity in underlying substrata and the ground-water. The major area of salt-affected soils have high salinity indeed, the mean profile ECe being mostly between 18 to 65 mm hos. The salinity profile is variable however, in most of these soils, the highest value (particularly during summer) is observed in the surface 10-15 cm soil. In some situations there is another maxima at 80 to 150 cm soil depth. Sodium chloride and sodium sulphate are by far the dominant salts. The Sodium Absorption Ratio (SAR) for saturation extract is mostly between 35 to 95.

The soils are generally deep and have loam to clay loam texture. These are light grey brown and have angular blocky structure; occasionally in the form of large prism. Often these have a relatively dense lime nodular strata at depths of 60 to 120 cm. In a number of situations, highly saline water is present at depths 3-5 meters during the dry period of the year.

The lands invariably lie as wastelands. The high soil salinity permits a sparse cover of highly tolerant species like *Salvadora oleoides*, *Capparis aphylla*, *Cyperus rotundus*, *Sporobolus marginatus*, *Tamarix articulata*, *Prosopis julifilora* and *Dactyloc tenium sindicus* are also present. The grasses, provide but a very modest grazing. It is only during occasional wet year and consequent dilution of soil salinity that these grasses put on a substantial growth. Therefore, the present contribution of these lands to the economy of tract is very small indeed.

Potentials and the treatments needed for improvement of wastelands

The foregoing has clearly brought out the characteristics and limitations of the soils under various kinds of wastelands. Their potentiality and the scope for their improvement with required treatments is summarised in Table 13.2. While putting any techno-economic inputs on these lands for their improvement, the point that should be remembered is that their use should be judicious commensurating with their productivity-potential-overexploitation again will result in further degradation of soil and land, ultimately diminishing its productive potential, much of which is already lost.

Conclusion

Soils of wastelands of arid western Rajasthan and their charactristics are highly variable. We get highly sandy and wind erodible soils in some situations and shallow, gravelly and rocky soils with scanty vegetation in other locations. Saline soils also occupy sizeable area. The scanty vegetation cover present on these may apparently raise the doubt as regards the inherent capacity of these soils to support a reasonably good vegetative cover. However, the study of various soils occurring in this region indicates that these soils and lands are capable of sustaining a substantially increased vegetative cover. The region is also gifted with a large variety of plant species which can thrive one or the other habitat. The present low productivity is entirely due to immense degree of depletion that has occurred due to overexploitation of land. Whereas lands like those of sand dunes and sandy hummocks, sandy plains can be rehabilitated with less difficulty the others like gravelly, rolling plains and hard pan soils require greater effort and patience.

Table 13.2 : Use potentiality of wasteland soils

Kind of soil	Characteristics and properties	Present land use and scope for improvement
1. Soils of duny and hummocky sandy, plains	Highly sandy, deep, structureless, loose, porous soils with low moisture retention capacity. These are well supplied with various nutrient elements so as to support a healthy natural vegetation cover. However, the soils are highly susceptible to wind erosion and deflation processes.	Used as open pasture lands. Present landcover is in most situations in highly degraded and depleted state because of excessive, irrational grazing. Severe wind erosion hazard. Reseeding to improve quality and quantity of vegetation cover followed by controlled grazing. Shifting sand dunes and hummocks need in addition micro-wind barriers prior to these establishment treatment. The lands in 300 to 400 mm rainfall zone can sustain a silvi-pastoral cover for maximum productivity.
2. Hard pan soils	Shallow to moderately deep soil solum and hence root zone limitation and moderate moisture retention. Otherwise soils are fertile enough to support a healthy vegetation cover.	Open pasture lands. Present land cover highly degraded with large bare patches. The lands are fairly well suited for development into good pasture lands. Reseeding with high yielding perennial grasses followed by controlled grazing. Some stand of *Zizyphus rotundifolia* and *Acacia Tortilis* can be established by piercing the hard pan. This will permit some shade and aditional biomass.
3. Shallow gravely soils of gently sloping plains	Shallow to moderately deep, gravelly loamy sand to sandy loam soils. Patches of exposed bouldry strata. Considerable run-off because of gentle undulations. Soils are fertile enough.	7 to 20 per cent area under cropping. Rest used as open pasture lands. Present landcover highly degraded with large bare patches. The lands have the potential to be developed into moderately good pasture lands. Contour furrowing and staggard trenching are necessary to conserve moisture.

Table 13.2 : (Contd...)

4.	Soils of low hills and undulating gravelly plains	Very shallow to moderately deep gravelly sandy to sandy, loam	Open pasture lands with highly degraded vegetation cover comprising *Aristida* sp. and *Capparis* sp. The lands can be developed so as to provide a modest grazing. Some scope exists for contour furrowing and staggard trenching.
5.	Hills and gravelly piedmonts	Dissected, rugged plateaux, steep hills and gravelly piedmonts. Soil cover is very thin with large bare patches. In runnels and in patches in the piedmonts gravelly soils of some depth do occur—very low moisture retention capacity	Open grazing lands. Scanty vegetation cover. With special treatments like box trenching a thin stand of hardy trees like *Acacia Senegal* and *Prosopis juliflora* can be established. Besides, short grass like *Aristida* sp. can also be resceded to provide a very modest grazing. However, because of adverse soil and topographic condition, consequent high vulnerability to degradation. Strict control on grazing and cutting of trees is necessary.
6.	Salt-affected soils	The soils have mostly very high mean profile salinity. These are medium, occasionally fine, textured soils, often with a dense soil crust.	Open grazing lands with scanty soil vegetation cover. Reclamation not feasible because of paucity of fresh water and at places due to presence of highly saline waters close to surface. Same improvement in productivity possible through planting of tolerant species with special cultival and soil working techniques to create pockets of low salinity.

14

Soils of the Wastelands of Rajasthan*

C.T. Abichandani and *A.S. Kolarkar*

Introduction

Wastelands comprising of sand dunes and sandy plains are mostly prevalent in the arid zone of western Rajasthan, ravine-infested areas along the river Chambal and its tributaries in eastern Rajasthan, shallow skeletal lands skirting the Aravallis and other hilly ranges, and depressional lands and saline flats in the foothill regions.

Cultivable wasteland in the State occupies an area of 6,673 thousand hectares, about 19.6 per cent of the total area occupied by the State. Distribution of these cultivable wastelands in the State is largely conditioned by climatic factors. The cultivable wastelands of western Rajasthan, receiving rainfall only to an extent of 100 mm in the far desert region and 500 mm near Aravallis, account for nearly an area of 4,702 thousand hectares. Large areas of these cultivable wastelands occur in the districts of Bikaner, Jaisalmer, Barmer and Ganganagar. These lands are comprised of sandy terrains which may have flat, hummocky or rolling topography and receive rainfall below 250 mm. In eastern Rajasthan, considerable areas under cultivable wastelands occur in Chittorgarh, Bhilwada, Udaipur, Kota, Ajmer, Jaipur, Jhalawar and Tonk districts. These lands are of different textural

* Published in Proceedings of Symposium on "Wastelands in India", I.N.S.A., New Delhi, 1968.

classes, may be shallow to moderately deep and consist of deep rills and gullies.

There are about 5,207 thousand hectares of barren land occupying 14.3 per cent of the total area of the State. Large areas of land rendered barren, due to shifting sand dunes, occur in Jaisalmer, Barmer, Jodhpur, Sikar, Jalor and Nagaur districts. Barren lands comprising of rocky skeletal soils occur in the districts of Sirohi, Pali and Jodhpur. Saline flats and ranns occur scattered in the arid regions of western Rajasthan. In eastern Rajasthan, ravine-infested barren lands occur in Kota, Bundi, Sawai Madhopur and Jhalawar districts. Shallow rocky land abound in rest of the areas particularly in the districts adjoining Aravallis and other hilly ranges. Distribution of forests, barren lands, pastures, cultivable waste and old fallow lands in different districts of Rajasthan is given in Table 14.1 (Rajasthan Statistics, 1964).

Nature of Soils of Wastelands of Rajasthan

Several authors have described the nature of soils in different parts of the State. Raychaudhuri (1964) classified the soils of western Rajasthan into four classes according to rainfall pattern. Abichandani (1964) classified the soils of the arid zone of western Rajasthan into six groups on the basis of parent material and the mode of formation. Mehta (1968) has divided soils of Rajasthan into eight soil groups under twelve agroclimatic ones. From the studies conducted by the authors, the soils of the wastelands of Rajasthan can be broadly classified as under:

Undifferentiated sandy and droughty soils

These soils occur mainly in the districts of Bikaner, Jaisalmer, Barmer, Churu, Jhunjhunu, Ganganagar and Jodhpur, and are highly prone to wind erosion hazard. These could be broadly divided into the following three categories: (a) soils of shifting dunes, (b) soils of stabilised sand dunes, and (c) soils of sandy plains.

(a) Soils of shifting sand dunes

These are uniformly layered, very deep, and composed of fine sands with

Table 14.1: Distribution of land under non-agriculture in Rajasthan State (Area in thousand of hectares)

Sl. No.	District	Total geographical area	Forest		Area not available for cultivation				Cultivable land				Fallow other than current fallow	
					Land under non-agri-culture use		Barren		Permanent pastures		Cultivable waste			
			Area	%	Area	%	Area	%	Area	%	Area	%	Area	%
1.	Jhunjhunu	593	17	2.9	9	1.5	41	6.9	47	7.9	9	1.5	6	1.0
2.	Sikar	775	8	1.0	22	2.8	64	8.3	51	6.6	21	2.7	19	2.4
3.	Bikaner	2,720	10	0.4	99	3.6	17	0.6	19	0.7	1,779	65.4	233	8.6
4.	Churu	1,667	1	0.1	93	5.5	1	0.1	19	1.1	169	10.0	198	11.7
5.	Ganganagar	2,062	3	0.1	82	4.0	2	0.1	1	0.0	549	26.6	55	2.7
6.	Barmer	2,817	9	0.3	68	2.4	150	5.3	195	6.9	324	11.5	535	19.0
7.	Jaisalmer	3,883	19	0.5	47	1.2	1,635	42.1	77	2.0	1,691	43.5	217	5.6
8.	Jalore	1,056	4	0.4	33	3.1	98	9.3	49	4.6	27	2.6	108	10.2
9.	Jodhpur	2,253	1	0.0	76	3.4	156	6.9	115	5.1	73	3.2	617	27.4
10.	Nagaur	1,762	–	0.0	74	4.2	91	5.2	52	2.9	15	0.9	170	9.6
11.	Pali	1,222	60	4.9	49	4.0	160	13.1	80	6.5	20	1.6	184	15.1
12.	Sirohi	518	41	7.9	21	4.1	176	34.0	33	6.4	25	4.8	42	8.0
13.	Ajmer	833	36	4.3	43	5.1	108	12.1	61	7.3	153	18.3	42	5.0
14.	Alwar	768	20	2.6	31	4.0	149	19.4	24	3.1	56	7.2	6	0.7
15.	Banswara	507	39	7.7	6	1.1	143	28.2	38	7.5	25	4.9	51	10.0
16.	Bharatpur	808	14	1.7	39	4.8	157	19.4	24	3.0	37	4.5	13	1.6
17.	Bhilwara	1,046	14	1.3	40	3.8	165	15.7	91	8.7	328	31.3	141	13.4
18.	Bundi	562	27	4.8	27	4.8	199	35.4	33	5.9	48	8.5	12	2.1
19.	Chittorgarh	1,039	40	3.8	36	3.5	191	18.4	37	3.6	343	33.0	29	2.7
20.	Dungarpur	305	4	1.3	16	5.2	72	23.6	62	20.3	25	8.2	9	2.9
21.	Jaipur	1,400	38	2.7	67	4.8	122	8.7	125	8.9	159	11.3	74	5.2
22.	Jhalawar	619	18	2.9	26	4.2	123	19.8	45	7.3	108	17.4	19	3.0
23.	Kota	1,245	146	11.7	44	3.5	219	17.6	55	4.4	214	17.2	15	1.2
24.	Sawai Madhopur	1,052	42	3.9	31	2.9	306	29.1	93	8.8	96	9.1	15	1.4
25.	Tonk	719	9	1.2	23	3.2	58	8.1	62	8.6	143	19.9	14	1.9
26.	Udaipur	1,732	245	14.1	53	3.1	604	34.9	205	11.8	234	13.5	65	3.8
	Totel	33,983	865	2.5	1,155	3.4	5,207	15.3	1,693	4.98	6,673	19.6	2,889	8.5

an undulating or rolling topography. These dunes have been formed by aeolian action and comprise 90-96 per cent of sand of which nearly 80-85 per cent is fine sand. The soils are very loose, single grained and of pale brown colour. Calcium carbonate is present throughout the profile and pH usually ranges from 8.5 to 9.0. These soils are excessively drained due to rapid permeability and therefore have a very low moisture retention capacity. At field capacity one metre deep soil holds about 50-60 mm of available soil moisture.

These dune soils, because of having loose soil on the surface, always have about 3-4 per cent moisture in the subsoils at lower depths even during the hot months of April, May and June. This moisture status in the subsoils helps in the establishment of *Acacia tortilis* if planted during the onset of monsoon showers.

(b) Soils of stabilised sand dunes

These soils also have undulating to rolling topography. Texturally, these soil mainly comprise fine sands and have almost the same composition as that of shifting dunes, except that these have slightly higher percentage of silt and clay ranging up to 8 per cent. The soils are loose, single-grained with low water-holding capacity and rapid permeability, holding about 60-70 mm of available moisture per metre depth of soil. Calcium carbonate occurs throughout the profile, the concentration of which increases with depth. Small calcium carbonate concretions or nests are met with in the lower layers, particularly along the root channels. Because of the growth of the vegetation, soil profile dries up immediately after the cessation of monsoon.

(c) Soils of sandy plains

These are very deep soils, mostly comprising of sand and loamy sand up to the depth of 60 cm from the surface and underlain with gritty sandy loam. Land surface forms small to large hummocks, which shows evidence of wind action. Soil structure is single-grained and the concentration of calcium carbonate in the profile increases with depth. These lands remain as fallow for a considerable period and are cropped only once in five or six years. Such areas, abound in Jaisalmer, Bikaner, Barmer and Jodhpur districts.

Soils with kankar pans at shallow to moderate depths with different degree of indurations

These types of soils are common in many wasteland patches occurring generally on flat or gently-sloping lands in western Rajasthan. Such soils are also found as patches in grey brown soils as described by Mehta (1968). The soil texture ranges from loamy sand to loam and the soil depth varies from 10 to 40 cm. The soils are underlain either by hard concretionary lime layer of different degree of induration or by gravel pieces of granitic and rhyolitic origin, coated and partly cemented with lime. Such layers restrict both root and water penetration in the soil. On slopy lands, the top soil gets usually washed off, exposing the hard concretionary layer. A typical profile from Luni Block has the following composition as shown in Table 14.2.

Table 14.2 : A typical profile from Luni Block

Depth in cm	Gravel %	Coarse sand %	Fine sand %	Silt %	Clay %	$CaCO_3$ %	pH %
0-15	2.4	59.7	19.3	14.9	5.9	8.7	8.5
15-30	16.5	57.9	18.3	17.4	7.4	14.4	8.5
30-45	51.5	57.4	17.8	18.9	5.9	16.3	8.5

The second and third layers of such soils are gravelly and highly calcareous, and the layer below 30 cm is invariably hard, compact and highly indurated. Tall tree vegetation is uncommon on such lands. Mehta (1962) has also reported the occurrence of concretionary indurated layer in heavy black soils of Jhalawar district, 1/8th of the area of which is considered to be cultivable waste. The depth of the soil varies in thickness up to 40 cm and is underlain by weathered rock fragment of basaltic origin. The surface layers have dark brown colour and clayey texture, mixed with quartz, sandstone and basalt pieces of 5-7 cm in diameter. The soils have blocky structure, hard consistency and are slightly calcareous. Root penetration is significant in the top surface only. Similar types of soils of shallow to moderate depth with scattered gravel and rock fragments are also found in red loam soils in Dungarpur, Udaipur, Chittorgarh and Banswara districts (Mehta, 1968).

Most of the areas under these soils are wastelands, growing short grasses, and because of severe overgrazing these lands get eroded, exposing hard gravel surface and forming rills and gullies. There is a great need to protect these lands from further deterioration. Very shallow lands could be converted into good pasture lands with reseeding and controlled grazing. At places, where the top soil layer has substantial thickness of about 30 cm, crops can be cultivated during monsoon with proper soil management.

Saline and sodic soils

Major saline and sodic problems are found in the soils of the districts of Pali, Bhilwara, Bharatpur, Ajmer, Alwar, Jaipur, Jodhpur, Jalor, Tonk, Nagaur, Sirohi and Chittorgarh (Fireman and Ramamoorthy, 1962). In addition, Mehta (1968) has reported salinity problems in scattered areas in Udaipur, Sawai Madhopur, Bikaner, Jaisalmer and Barmer districts also. Abichandani and Kolarkar (1967) have broadly classified saline soils of western Rajasthan into three groups, namely (i) old saline soils formed from continental salt wash and which accumulated in depressions and lagoons, (ii) saline soils of recent origin, formed due to the rise in the level of saline groundwaters, and (iii) soils of secondary salinization made saline due to continuous use of saline groundwater for irrigation.

The old saline soils of medium to very high salinity occur scattered in patches, commonly known as 'ranns'. Some of these are located in the natural depressional areas serving as drainage basins for surrounding lands. These have highly saline groundwaters at 1-3 metres depth and the soils are of medium to heavy texture, ranging from loams to clay loams and clays at lower depths, with a surface mantle of coarse textured deposits. The soil pH is about 8.0 to 8.5. The salts in the profile are unevenly distributed and the total soluble salt in the surface soil is usually over one per cent but may sometimes rise to 5-6 per cent and the crust on the surface may contain salts as high as 25 per cent. Dominant salt usually is sodium chloride.

Aridity development in the area resulted in wind-borne sand deposits which choked up the natural drainage of these areas with the result that surface-drained water from surrounding high lands continuously accumulates in these locations and develops more or less into ponds. Draining of these low-lying basins and providing proper drainage where the same have been choked up will greatly help to ameliorate the saline conditions in these lands and also of the surrounding lands, thus reducing the further spread of salinity.

In certain wastelands of western Rajasthan, patchy salinity has developed, particularly in the arid zone region where water table is 6-7 metres deep. The soluble salts in such soils have a preponderance of calcium. These soils occur in slight depressional locations and tend to develop salinity in small and big patches which range in size from 2 to 7 sq metres. These patches show a characteristic feature of moist appearance on the surface, whereas the non-saline surrounding areas are dry. Sand fraction in these soils ranges, from 70 to 85 per cent and the clay is about 13 per cent in top soil and less than 8 per cen below 100 cm depth. Salinity in these soils decreases with depth from 2 per cent and above in top soil to below 0.5 per cent at 100 cm depth. These soils are comparatively easy to reclaim. As these areas are in slight depressions, rainwater from surrounding areas helps to push the salts down below the sand and gravel layer, which occurs at 150 to 200 cm depth. The preponderance of calcium salts in soil solution helps to maintain the soil condition such that will facilitate downward movement of water and thus help in leaching the salts down the soil column. Screening of various plant species suited to various soil salinity levels and their plantation in such lands will go a long way to ameliorate the conditions in absence of good quality water for reclamation of these lands. Screening of salt-resistant grass species and cultivating these in such lands would also give a better utilization of these lands.

In some of the wastelands in western Rajasthan, formation of saline soil is of recent origin and is formed as a result of rise in saline groundwater, particularly in the Nimblana, Reothria and Bagra areas. The formation of such soils has been accelerated by human agency. In these parts, the natural flow of surface run-off water has been interrupted with dykes and led to dug ponds for stock drinking and human consumption and at other places the water has been diverted to low-lying areas for *rabi* cultivation. Ponding and seepage of these waters in the soil has led to a rise in saline groundwater-table. In some places, groundwater has low salinity, nearly 1-2 gm/litre, but continuous capillary rise of the water leads to salinity and sodic problems in these soils.

The problem of soil salinity due to the rise in the water-table also needs special attention. As mentioned, the rise in the groundwater-table at these places has been caused by human agency as a result of diverting the inflow of surface water from the surrounding areas. It is, therefore, necessary to conduct hydrological surveys of these areas to find out the direction of subsurface hydrostatic pressures and plot out the directions of water recharge in such areas. The recharge flows of such water could then be successfully diverted to other areas and thereby minimise the further rise in ground water-table. Salt tolerant trees and shrub species can be planted on such salt-affected soils to serve as aid in soil amelioration and provide plant covers for grazing and for fuel and timber (Bernstein, 1960).

Shallow to moderately deep soils of gravelly and skeletal nature along hill aprons on 3 to 5 per cent slopes

The soils of these wastelands are under continuous erosional process, firstly due to their physiographic position, which receives the run-off water from the adjoining hill ranges, and secondly due to their slope gradients which range from 3 to 5 per cent. As a result, these soils have gravels, cobbles and stones, both on the surface and also mixed in the soil matrix. Such soils are also found in certain table lands, especially in arid parts, where wind erosion has blown away the top soil and exposed the gravelly under terrain. These soils are, however, common on slopes along the hilly terrain.

A typical soil profile of the wasteland of Jalor area shows 15 cm of pale brown to light brown gravelly, non-calcareous loamy sand soil with profuse roots overlying highly gravelly, somewhat compact, non-clacareous loamy sand up to 30 cm depth and rock fragments and cobbles coated with lime below. Vegetation like *Euphorbia nerifolia*, *Commiphora mukul*, *Grevia populifolia* and *Codia rothii* are commonly found on such soils.

Similar soils of varying depth have been reported from hill ranges of Jhalawar district (Mehta, 1962). These soils have top 30 cm of slightly calcareous dark red loam mixed with gravel and sandstone fragment and have many roots. Below this, up to 75 cm depth, the soils contain yellowish-red, slightly calcareous loam mixed with large fragments of weathered rocks.

Such skeletal soils also occur in Pali district in the Jawai command area and have top 22 cm of yellowish-brown non-calcareous sandy loam with few roots mixed with gravel on the surface. Below this, up to 45 cm, dark yeallowish-brown, highly gravelly sandy loam soil occurs and this is underlain by weathered granitic rock fragment with lime incrustations.

These shallow skeletal soils need proper soil conservation measures for agriculture, pasture and forestry development, depending on soil nature and soil depths.

Hydromorphic soils of low-lying depressional areas

The hydromorphic soils of the wastelands of Rajasthan are characterised by the presence of excess of water during monsson due either to inflow of surface flood water or by capillary rise of groundwater through the profile, or by temporary waterlogging of certain soil horizons. In the arid region, this type of soil develops only in depressional patches where rain or flood water from nearby streams accumulates.

The profile of hydromorphic soil is of fairly uniform character. The parent material on which the soil is formed is usually calcareous clay or clay loam deposited in depression in the older alluvium or in the recently abandoned dead stream channel beds. Soils at lower depths contain rusty-coloured traces of iron oxide, usually in streaks along root channels. Light grey coloured mottlings indicative of reduced condition are also common in the soil profile. The surface soil is poor in organic matter and is frequently of platy structure. Further down, the soil structure becomes blocky and then gradually merges into its parent material. At many places, the soil surface shows wide fissures forming fairly regular hexagons. After the cessation of monsoon, the soils are invariably waterlogged at lower depths. At some places, the soils show variability in texture down the profiles due to variations in nature of parent material deposits. Sometimes, sandy layer overlies a clayey stratum or clayey soil overlies a calcareous friable sandy alluvium. At places, these soils are saline in the lower depths. A typical profile of hydromorphic soils from Jalor area has the following characteristics:

0-15 cm	Greyish brown to dark greyish brown loam to clay loam, platy, hard, slightly calcareous; many fine roots.
15-60 cm	Dark greyish brown to very dark grey brown clay, subangluar to angular blocky, slightly calcareous; mixed with small brown to black concretions; few fine roots.
60-90 cm	Light olive brown to olive brown clay loam, mixed with lime concretions, coated reddish brown, very hard compact layer, highly calcareous; no roots.

In western Rajasthan, such hydromorphic soils occur as beds or broken belts in the low lands corresponding to old abandoned disorganised drainage channels as reported by Ghosh (1965). The soils of these abandoned channels have, however, water-worked gravel beds and sands at depth of 2-3 metres and below. With adequate reclamation and amelioration these wastelands could be put under fairly good unirrigated *rabi* cultivation.

Soils of highly eroded, gullied and ravine areas

Water erosion is one of the greatest problems in eastern Rajasthan, especially in the districts of Kota, Bundi, Sawai Madhopur and Jhalawar, where medium to heavy-textured soils predominate. Out of about 4 lakh hectares of Chambal command area, falling in districts of Bundi and Kota, nearly 23 per cent area is ravine-infested wasteland, and another 10 per cent area suffers from active sheet erosion each year.

The soils of these gullied and ravine-infested wastelands comprise mostly of fluvial deposits of the past, which are very deep, and with the concentration of calcium carbonate increasing with depth. The colour of the surface soil varies from grey to brown, but due to the presence of lime, the soil at depths below 120 cm generally exhibits yellowish brown colour. Soil texture ranges from silt loam, clay loam to silty clays. Soils are generally heavier up to about 120 cm depth but below this gradually become comparatively lighter. The surface soil has crumb to granular structure while at lower depths structure is blocky and prismatic. Layers below 120 cm depth, however, are generally hard and compact. Lime concretions of varying sizes from pin head to peanut size are generally found scattered in the matrix and increase in size and number with depth. Root penetration is good up to 120 cm depth.

These sails of variable composition have the least resistance to water erosion both as particle size and as cohesive material and are therefore prone to form gullies of extremely variable sizes and depths, which have in the past developed into shallow to deep ravines. Mehta *et al.* (1958) investigating physical properties and erodibility of these soils, observed that the gullies in these soils tend to deepen because of increased erodibility of the subsoil layers. He stated that although the nature of surface soil layers is of importance in the study of erosion behaviour, the lower strata have a far more decisive bearing not only on the extent of damage but also on the type and intensity of erosion which may occur in these soils. A soil profile from Kota district studied by Mehta (1958) had following composition and other physical characteristics as shown in Table 14.3.

Table 14.3 : A Soil profile from Kota district

Depth in cm.	*$CaCO_3$ %*	*Sand %*	*Clay %*	*Silt %*	*Dispersion ratio*	*Erosion ratio*	*Clay ratio*
0-25	1.6	38.80	25.22	33.78	16.40	18.0	2.90
25-90	3.9	36.68	29.08	30.34	26.00	29.8	2.30
90-115	18.2	19.23	27.05	35.52	45.60	44.1	2.02
115-180	31.1	14.70	22.10	31.50	77.50	71.7	2.02

These soils have high dispersion and erosion ratios, which increase with depth and are therefore prone to severe water erosion hazard. If proper care is taken to conserve the upper layers of these soils further erosion damage in the formation of rills, gullies and ravines could be avoided.

Many gullied and ravine areas could be reclaimed for profitable use and at places for cultivation as these areas still have fairly deep and fertile soils. Individual farmers have to be induced to take up such areas for reclamation, with technical assistance. Gullies which cannot be reclaimed for cultivation need be stabilized by fencing and by seeding with suitable grasses, planting suitable trees and shrubs and wherever necessary putting brush dams of check dams so that the further deepening of these is checked.

The soils of wastelands of Rajasthan categorically thus fall mainly under Classes IV, V, VI and VII large areas being considered fit for pasture development only. As mentioned earlier, the land use in Rajasthan is largely conditioned by climatic and soil factors and as such large areas of wastelands either lie in the arid tracts of western Rajasthan or in the gullied lands of eastern Rajasthan. In addition, large areas of land, about 2,890 thousand hectares, accounting for about 8.5 per cent of the total area of State, comprise of old and long fallows, which are put under cultivation once in three to five years. Utilization and amelioration of such large tracts of wasteland of Rajasthan have therefore to be viewed in relation to adverse climatic condition and large livestock population that subsist on forage from these lands. In spite of this, large areas of wasteland, particularly in rainfall regions of 300 mm and above with good soil depth, could be brought into cultivation. Rehabilitation of some of these wastelands in this State also demands provision of irrigation facilities, development of protected grazing areas to sustain large livestock population and amelioration of ravine-infested lands. Rehabilitation of wastelands of sandy terrains in the arid region demands a systematic programme of dune afforestation to check movements of shifting sands and thus protect the adjoining lands already under the plough.

REFERENCES

Abichandani, C.T. (1964). "Genesis, Morphology and Management of Arid Zone Soils of Western Rajasthan". In : *Symposium on Problems of Indian Arid Zone,* UNESCO and Ministry of Education, Jodhpur.

Abichandani, C.T., and Kolarkar, A.S.(1967). "Soil Salinity Problems in the Arid Zone of Western Rajasthan." *North Zonal Workshop in Soil Science.* I.C.A.R.. PAU, Hissar.

Bernstein, L. (1960). "Salt affected soils and plants on the problems of the Arid Zone". In : *Proceedings of the UNESCO Symposium,* Paris.

Fireman, M., and Ramamoorthy, B. (1962). "A comparison of the major saline and alkali areas in India with those in U.S.A." In : *Seminar on Salinity and Alkali Soil Problems,* I.A.R.I., New Delhi.

Ghosh, Bimal (1965). "The genesis of the desert plains in the Central Luni basin of Western Rajasthan." *J. Indian Soc. Soil Sci.*, 13.

Mehta, K.M. (1962). *Report on soil and crop investigation of Jawai project area.* Agril. Chemistry Sect., Dept. of Agric., Rajasthan, Udaipur.

Mehta, K.M., Mathur, C.M., and Shankaranarayan, H.S. (1958). "Investigation on the physical properties of Kota soils in relation to their erodibility." *J. Indian Soc. Soil Sci.*, 6.

Mehta, K.M. *et al.* (1962). *Report on the Soil Survey and Classification of Jhalawar District.* Dept. of Agri., Rajasthan Agri, Chemistry Section, Udaipur.

——,(1968). "Proposed agroclimatic zone of Rajasthan." *In Symposium on New Cropping Pattern*, I.C.A.R., New Delhi.

Raychaudhuri, S.P. (1964). "Classification and fertility of soils of desert and semi-desert regions in India." In : *Symposium on Problems of Indian Arid Zone*, UNESCO and Ministry of Education, Jodhpur.

15

Wastelands and their Better Use through Soil Survey

S.V. Govinda Rajan

Introduction

The proper utilization of the land and soil resources of a State or a country is a matter of utmost concern to its community or people. Sail is the most valuable natural resource of the State and its proper utilization for production of agricultural, forestry or other crops which besides adding to the much needed foodstuffs required to feed the human and animal population, results in the addition of wealth of the community. All lands and all soils are naturally not of the same value for utilisation for production of above types of wealth, since their properties and qualities vary to a great deal based on differences in their situation, formation, fertility level, productivity, etc. Some lands are good for production because their soils are good, and in recognition of these properties such lands are readily put to use and their productivity exploited readily. Other lands because of unfavourale conditions affecting their situation, or the formations of soils occurring on them not being satisfactory, and in consequence are exploited less readily, less effectively or less efficiently. Yet other types of lands exist which because of the very unsatisfactory conditions of the soil alone or in combination with external factors associated with their location, are so unremunerative that they are left unutilised and lie in the condition of a "wasteland". The mere fact that some types of land are lying unutilised or neglected does not necessarily mean that they are unfit to be utilised for useful production. A variety of factors may be operative which render such lands to remain in a condition of non- utilization and a proper examination of these factors through study of the soils, terrain features or the conditions of the landholdings, can enable an assessment of these and a means can be found for utilising the lands for better purpose.

Classification of Wastelands

Wastelands commonly include those lands which can be considered culturable waste other than fallow lands. The utilization of such cultivable lands for cultivation and further exploitation is very important in any plan for expansion of cultivation. Planning for the potential resources from such lands after development requires reliable information regarding the extent of such cultivable lands which can be available to the concerned agencies. The category "culturable waste" has been defined to include all lands available for cultivation but not taken up for cultivation. Besides lands considered as culturable waste, (i) lands under permanent pastures and meadows, (ii) areas under miscellaneous trees and crops, and (iii) fallows other than current fallows have also been included in the wasteland category by the Committee set up by Planning Commission in 1962 to consider Wasteland Survey and Reclamation. The Committee pointed out that the concept of the category of lands classified as "other uncultivated lands excluding fallow lands" has not yet been clearly understood. This is because in the classification it is difficult to decide which of these lands are permanently incapable of cultivation and which are cultivable but are being classified as barren and uncultivable or pasture lands. Only rational and scientifically carried out field surveys can enable a proper classification of these lands as regards to their actual capability. Without scientific means of investigating the properties of the soil or judging their potentialities for considering them to be culturable or otherwise by means of soil surveys, it is quite difficult for any revenue agency to group the lands into the correct categories, whereas in any planning for development, correct estimates of the potential land resources for further development are made. The records furnished by the revenue agency of each state are the sources from which the required information about the land utilization and the availability of lands for further development can be drawn upon, and with the lacuna as indicated above existing, it is to be expected that it is difficult to estimate or forecast the potential extent for such exploitation or the location of such lands.

Soil Surveys in Wastelands

The criteria to determine whether land deserves to be classified as unclutivable wasteland or whether it can be put under the plough, do not demand the large or wide range of data that are normally collected through detailed soil surveys. It should normally be adequate if only a limited numbr of items of information are available from soil surveys, on the basis of which a decision can be arrived at regarding the capability of the soil for cultivation and production of crops and to make an assessment of the limiting factors that are operative on the land and the remedial measures that may be needed to make the land fit for satisfactory cultivation. The other soil and landscape details, when collected through the survey, will help in formulating a detailed analysis for classification into land capability subgroups and units. This information may be useful for drawing up measures of reclamation or remedial measures to overcome the limitations or hazards operating on these wastelands, and also may be acquired for management of the lands fit for cultivation for production on a sustained basis.

It will be appropriate to describe here some examples of the use of soil survey data for lands lying waste and the recommendations that are made for the better utilization of these lands on the basis of their capabilites. Two areas, one in Maharashtra and the other in West Bengal, where soil surveys were done to suggest proper use of the wastelands, are described here.

Soils of Certain Wastelands in Maharashtra State

Extensive areas in the Nanded and Aurangabad Divisions of Maharashtra are lying as uncultivated wastes on account of their locations, terrain features and such other factors. They are usually on steep lands, and are severely eroded with thin soil cover, and the vegtation is poor. They are neither put to use for cultivation nor for pasture. A survey of these areas was taken up by the All India Soil and Land Use Survey to study the soils and to give recommendations for their uses. The total area involved was 4,317 acres and divided into 7 blocks distributed in three ranges of the Forest Department. A description of the terrain and soil features of two of the Blocks and the recommendations made for the use of the lands are summarised here.

Wadgaon Block

The Block has a total area of 1250 acres and lies to the west of Wadgaon village located about 11 miles to the north of Osmanabad town. The area is situated on a plateau divided into two parts by a deep gully which runs from east to west. The southern half is severely eroded, and many gullies both shallow and deep, run over the whole area from east to west and south-west which is the normal direction of the slope, and which ranges from 5 to 50 per cent. The entire area is highly undulating and erosion is severe. The shallow soil is gravelly to gravelly clay loam and the profile has following characteristics :

Depth	*Description*
0-5 cms	Reddish brown (5 YR 5/4 dry, 5YR 4/3 moist) gravelly clay loam, single grain structure, dry and lose. No mottling or concretions, boundary clear and smooth. No effervescence with HCl. Root penetration good.
5 cms and over	Weathered disintegrating rock yielding reddish brown, loose murrum. Dry, few roots.

The relief of the area is excessive with undulating steep slopes. The vegetation is scanty grass. Erosion is severe and the drainage is excessive. The soil is dry, and grass root penetration is restricted to about 10 cms.

Recommendations

The steeply undulating nature of the terrain has resulted in severe sheet and gully erosion. The soil depth is in the range of 5 to 8 cms, below which is murrum. Since these lands are not fit for cultivations, they are kept under Land Use capability Class VI. Afforestation is recommended, with grassing at suitable locations. On steep slopes of 25 to 50 per cent contour, trenching is needed to retain the moisture and to prevent rapid erosion. On lower slopes bunding is suggested as a soil and moisture conservation measure.

Ghatangri Block

This block, measuring 355 acres, lies to the north of Osmanabad at a distance of 4 miles towards Bhir. The topography is steep and undulating with shallow to deep gullies. The average slope is 10 per cent but on the western side it is as high as 35 per cent. In the southern portion of the block small patches occur with soil of good depth. The entire area is lying uncultivated and waste. The soils are mainly of two types : (i) very shallow, dark brown gravelly clay loam and (ii) medium deep, dark reddish-brown clay soil in localised patches in the South.

Shallow soil

Depth	*Description*
0-8 cms	Dark brown (10 YR 4/3 dry, to YR 3/3 moist) gravelly clay loam, single grain, loose, dry. No lime concretions or effervescence with HCl. Boundary abrupt and smooth. Grass roots present.
8 cms and over	Weathered rock yielding murrum with gritty pieces of angular quartz.

Relief of the area is excessively undulating with slopes in the range of 20 to 25 per cent towards west. Scanty grass vegetation, with good root distribution, up to 8 cms. Excessively drained.

Medium deep soil

Depth	*Description*
0-15 cms	Dark reddish-brown (5 YR 3/2 dry) clay, sub-

	angular blocky structure, hard breaking into small clods. No lime. Boundary diffuse. Dry.
15-35 cms	Dark reddish-brown (5 YR 3/2) clay soil. Sub-angular blocky structure, moist, and very firm. No lime. Roots present. Boundary abrupt and smooth.
35 cms and over	Weathered disintegrated rock and murrum with gritty quartz pieces. Freely drained.

Brief description of the soil profile of two types of soils is given here.

The relief of the area is concave depression and erosion moderate with sheet and rill erosion. The vegetation consists of scanty grass and drainage is imperfect. Surface scan is dry, but subsoil is moist.

Recommendations

The shallow soil conditions on the slopy lands show that the land is not considered fit for cultivation and these are placed in capability Class VI. Afforestation with suitable species like *babul, neem, acacia, siamia* and *karanji* can be profitably tried. The areas under the medium deep soil are classified under land capability Class IV. Cultivation with the dry crops adapted to the area are recommended. Soil and moisture conservation measures should be adopted to get satisfactory results.

Wastelands along the Teesta bed in West Bengal

Certain areas in the flood plains of the river Teesta in Jalpaiguri district which are lying as wastelands were surveyed to assess the suitability for settling refugee cultivators. The soils in these lands are formed by riverine depositions and as they are still young in development, well defined profile formation has not taken place. These "Char" land or flood plain soils have remained fallow due to repeated inundation and vegetation of wild growth of *Typha latifolia, Typha angustifolia*, "Nal". "Bhabri" and related species have taken hold over much of the areas. Physiographically, this area is divisible into the following three types : (i) high lands, (ii) flat lands, and (iii) bottom lands and depressions.

The soils of the fiat land are briefly described here and the capability classes into which these lands can be placed to aid programme of better utilization of these lands which are lying waste are also indicated in the recommendations.

Flat land soils Mouza-Purba Premganj, P.S.-Mal, District-Jalpaiguri.

Depth	Description
0-15 cms	Grey (5 Y 5/1 dry) loamy soil, cloddy and subangular blocks. Soft in consistency when wet and friable when dry. Few dark brown (10 YR 4/3) mottlings, moist, concretions nil and root distribution numerous.
15-23 cms	Olive grey (5 Y 5/2 moist) sandy loam, structureless when wet and loose when dry. Concretions nil, but mottlings (very dark grey brown 2.5 Y 3/2) present. Root distribution few.
23 to 70 cms	Light grey (5 Y 7/2) coarse sand. Single grain structure, loose incoherent mass, no mottlings, no concretions. Water-table below 70 cms.

Relief of the area is generally flat with a maximum slope of 5 per cent. The vegetation consists of thick growth of "Nal" and "Bhabri". The groundwater is high and drainage imperfect in many places.

Recommendations

From field observation it is seen that the better drained flat lands can be put under land capability Class II while those subject to high water-table can go under Class V. The Class II lands can be put under cultivation by Aus and Aman paddy and Jute and in the dry season by groundnut (erect varieties). Addition of suitable amounts of organic. matter and fertilizers to supply to plant nutrients in which the soils are deficient are recommended. Drainage is required to be improved in areas subject to high water-table. The Class V lands subject to inundation by the river waters, are fit for pasture.

Conclusion

Soil surveys furnish information about the soils of any area which are basic for any programme of land utilization, whether it be for agricultural purpose, forestry development, urban utilization or engineering operations such as high-way layout, development of airports etc. The soils of "wastelands" also required to be studied in a scientific manner through soil surveys and the information thus collected would enable a proper appraisal of the capability of the wastelands for utilization for agriculture purposes or other related uses and for developing a programme for efficient management of the soils for sustained production.

Index